WAR EAGLE

Texas Cherokee

Martha Lou Perritti

ISBN: 978-1-58320-040-7
Printed in the USA by Lifestyles Press

For my son,

Richard Victor Perritti

Also by Martha Lou Perritti

Crossing in the Rain

Standing Against the Wind

From this Fertile Valley

Ribbon of Time

Cooking Our Way

Martha Lou's Kitchen

Contents

PART FOUR

PART FIVE

Preface

By examining historical facts, which are shrouded by the spirits of the Native American people, we search for the truth of life as it was lived by those who are often forgotten.

Our minds and our hearts are open as we explore the lands of the Red River Valley. The Red River runs through this valley, separating the states of Oklahoma and Texas.

From the Red River Valley to Tahlequah, Oklahoma, to the gold fields of California, back to Texas, it is interesting to discover how the events of history determine the character of one person who traveled this trail.

Time fades the memory of all those who came before; revisiting places and people refreshes the memories and feeds the soul.

War Eagle is born in a time of turbulence in American history. He must learn to fight for two freedoms. War Eagle takes up the gauntlet not only for the freedom of America, but also for freedom for the Texas Cherokee.

Enduring love and friendship color this story of War Eagle, Little Bear, Polly, Sam Houston, and many others. Some characters are real and famous; others are fictional in name but embody the spirit of that time and place.

I am flooded with emotions as I write about the Cherokee people. I am reminded that all races have endured times of repression. Only the passing of years will right the wrongs. The pain of so many is shared in tracing the footsteps of past generations. We must push past the pain to secure a better tomorrow.

The path we follow determines our future. One thing is certain: no matter what path War Eagle followed, he forever remained a Texas Cherokee.

PART ONE

CHAPTER ONE

Sky Walker Meets Bright Flower

An eagle soared over the peaceful Red River Valley; the sunset cast shadows on the river's water as a young Indian maiden knelt to fill her water jar.

Wiping his brow, Sky Walker stepped into the underbrush to hide himself while watching her.

Alone, she seemed in no hurry while the gentle flow of pristine water filled her jar. As she lifted her head to the call of the eagle, her beautiful long, black hair rested gently upon her small shoulders.

Sky Walker was captivated by her graceful movement. Was she real or just a longing vision? Only one way to find out; he would follow her the short distance back to the village.

Anxious not to lose sight of her, Sky Walker jumped on his horse bareback, a blanket serving as a saddle, and held the end of a lariat tied around the horse's neck. All this movement had most likely captured the eyes of the maiden.

Once he was sure of which cabin she entered, Sky Walker moved quickly and disappeared into the woods.

She had not seen his face and was not sure if he was a suitor.

"Bright Flower," her mother said as she opened the cabin door, "do you know the young man who has followed you home?" "Mother, I do not know this person or what he looks like.

The flight of the birds from the underbrush down by the river gave me notice of his presence."

"We will find out who he is and what he looks like before he approaches you. If it turns out he is a desirable suitor, you will need a chaperone before you meet again."

What Mother said and what really happened were often different stories, as Bright Flower soon found out.

The low, winter sun soon sank in the sky. The whippoorwill sang with spirit to Sky Walker while he chopped the wood to fuel the fire to warm the house where he lived with his family. The hooting owl reigned in the night, as he lay awake. For certain, he had found the girl of his dreams. Now he must go about inducing her to listen to his suit.

Nights of the winter were long, and the bitter cold was hard to bear. Keeping the family safe, as healthy as possible, and from starvation came before any plans for romance.

Often on the warpath and forever on the hunt for food, Sky Walker joined all Texas Cherokee in the quest for survival. The natural environment provided life to the Cherokee people. It was a hard life. The natural elements made everyone acutely observant of the earth.

Preparation for the sweeping cold air of the winter months was communal, as everyone and everything had a role and responsibility.

When they could, the women gathered wild plants for food and medicines. The men were skilled hunters; killing large animals, such as deer, bear, and buffalo as well as smaller game, such as rabbits, raccoons, and turkeys.

Building the Cherokee village along the Red River provided access to fresh water and different kinds of fish for food. Come the warm days of summer, the banks of the river became the battleground of love's warfare.

The winter season had only delayed the courtship of Sky Walker and Bright Flower; this experience would be shared by most all of the Texas Cherokee who lived in the Red River Valley.

As the earth was dressed anew in the fresh and living beauty of springtime, Sky Walker prepared to meet the young maiden.

By the wisdom of Bright Flower's mother, she had found out not only what the possible suitor looked like, but also who he was. Most important, the fact that he was of the Cherokee tribe but not of the same clan made Sky Walker a desirable suitor.

Respecting tradition, Mother advised her daughter, "From now on, you must go with a chaperone to all public affairs and especially to the river."

An evening breeze cooled the pressing heat of the summer day. As she came from the river, he approached her, taking up a position directly in her path. She was willing to stop and listen.

She put down on the ground the jar of water she was carrying. Her chaperone stepped aside while he introduced himself. "They call me Sky Walker."

Softly, she said, "My name is Bright Flower." This first meeting was a beginning. He waited for her to walk away, and then he turned on his path through a field of wildflowers along the bank of the river. He was twenty-six. The years had brought him to this field of flowers for his soul to enjoy and to find the love of his life. Her name: Bright Flower.

Autumn leaves would fall from the trees before the wedding would take place. The courtship between Sky Walker and Bright Flower was no secret, and it appeared that the entire tribe of the Texas Cherokee was eager to be involved in a marriage ceremony.

Carefully planned to be blessed by the priest, the event would at the same time be full of customs and ideas of a frivolous or superficial character.

It took seven days to prepare a sacred spot for the ceremony, and hours before the wedding, a welcoming fire burned brightly. To witness this Cherokee wedding, hundreds crowded the area along the banks of the Red River.

A pathway was cleared for the approaching wedding party. Standing with her mother and older brother, Bright Flower had a blue blanket around her shoulders. Sky Walker joined her as a member of his family placed a blue blanket around him.

The Cherokee priest spoke of the people who first walked the lands they now call "home." On this day, a new journey begins for Bright Flower and Sky Walker to build their life together. We will be a source of harmony and balance for them, he said.

The blue blankets were removed from the couple's shoulders. They now stood together as the priest wrapped a white blanket around them, uniting them as one.

For a moment, it seemed as if the noon sun stood still; the Cherokee priest gave his blessing.

Silence and reverence soon gave way to festive laughter and joyous celebration. A wedding feast had been prepared. The couple drank from the wedding vase and everyone rejoiced in the occasion.

Not until the day was tinged with the red of sunset did the couple slip away. The dancing and celebration would continue throughout the night as Bright Flower and Sky Walker made their way into the wilderness. In true native tradition, they listened to the wind blowing through the pine trees, waiting to hear messages from the spirits.

Time was not measured; only the rising and setting of the sun counted the days the couple spent in seclusion. Bright Flower and Sky Walker returned to the village as man and wife.

CHAPTER TWO

History of Cherokee

Historical research reveals the presence of people in America in 13,000 BCE. By 9,000 BCE, Paleo-Indians were established throughout the Western Hemisphere.

There were 550 different tribes of American Indians. The existence of these people depended on the natural environment. Their thinking and cultures were determined by all things natural in the world.

It was a hard life, with everyone understanding his or her responsibility as the tribe acutely observed the earth.

The enormous power of nature was felt when they looked at the stars and realized how vast the sky is. During the day, they saw clouds rolling across the blue sky, often bringing a rainstorm.

Sometimes rivers flooded, and there were dangerously powerful tornadoes.

Everything had a role to play in this land of plains, towering mountains, and vast amounts of space.

The wilderness was a land of plenty. Heavy forest clothed the sloping sides of the mountains. Streams ran down from the mountains, and along the banks of these streams were many elk and deer. Here and there, the streams were dammed by the beaver, and the brooks were alive with trout.

Within the forest, there were lakes with many islands where moose and bear were abundant. A great variety of birds filled the forest. The whippoorwill sang with spirit, and the hooting owl reigned in the night. The crane, the swan, the loon, and many smaller birds did not go unnoticed. Along the outskirts of the heavy forest rose clusters of housing for the native people. Shortly after 500 BC, Native Americans began to settle in villages along the Red River, in the area of the United States of America now known as the Red River Valley of Texas.

Along with the benefits of the river waters, this territory had a piney forest. Many other kinds of trees also grew in the piney woods. Hardwood trees such as oak, pecan, walnut, and the bois d'arc provide good nuts to eat along with their wood. The bois d'arc is perfect for making bows for shooting arrows, a weapon used for hunting and for war.

This region had a good climate for farming; corn, beans, and squash provided the main source of food. Other foods gathered by the native women were wild—acorns, black berries, persimmons, roots, and other plants and fruits.

Perhaps most important to the survival of the Native Americans were the herds of buffalo that dotted the rolling plains. Hunting parties of men sometimes traveled long distances to find the buffalo. In order to carry the meat home, the men would dry it for preservation. They saved the skins to tan and use as robes. Buffalo skins with the hair on them are very soft and warm.

In the fall and winter months, the native people would set fires in the woods to burn away the old, tall grass, small shrubs, and bushes without hurting the old trees with fluid bark. In the spring, the new green grass would get more sun and grow better on the burned areas than in the undergrowth. The tender green grass attracted animals to hunt and made it easier to find acorns and nuts on the ground.

The native people of this land found ways to control their environment without destroying nature's earth.

CHAPTER THREE

White Man's Invasion

The winds of time blew across these lands where everything fit together and the people lived in harmony with nature.

In a distant place, a different people grew restless. Filled with a yearning for riches, they searched for a path to find their gold.

These invaders reached the shores of the Western Hemisphere in 1492, when an Italian, Christopher Columbus, landed his ships on an island in the Bahamas, southeast of what is now known as Florida.

Columbus was convinced that it would be possible to reach Asia by sailing west from Europe instead of east. When Columbus arrived in America, he thought he was in the East Indies and called the people he met "Indians."

The land Columbus found was not Asia, but his voyages opened up the white man's settlement of the Western Hemisphere.

No single culture of Indians was dominant in the region found by Columbus and the European explorers that followed. Many different peoples inhabited the area. The fates of European explorers and settlers depended on whether a tribe was kind or warlike. Friendly tribes taught newcomers hunting methods and how to grow indigenous crops and prepare foods. Warlike tribes made life difficult and dangerous. Most Native Americans resisted conquest by these European newcomers.

One of the principal Indian nations in the Western Hemisphere was called Cherokee or Ani-Yonwiya, the "Principal People."

The Cherokee Iroquoian language and migration legends suggest that the tribe originated north of the area in which the Europeans first encountered them.

The Cherokees' first contact with Europeans came in 1540.

A Spanish expedition led by Hernando de Soto passed through Cherokee territory. More than a hundred years passed before French and English traders began appearing regularly. The 1670s marked the beginning of sustained contact between the two cultures.

Being a friendly, settled, agricultural people, the Cherokee were quick to adopt many material elements of European culture.

Due to the process of European empire building in the Native American homeland, the Cherokee were subjected to calamitous wars, epidemics, and food shortages. As a result, the Cherokee population declined, their territory shrank, and their group identity weakened.

The French, the Spanish, and the English all wanted control of the newfound continent. They fought wars against each other, the Cherokee siding with one and then the other. The Native Americans were not the winners in any of these conflicts.

From Columbus's landing in 1492, it was over 200 years before European settlers united under one flag and declared their independence from all of the European countries.

The European settlers fled their homelands to escape problems their cultures had created. Determined to establish a new way of life, these people adopted the Declaration of Independence in 1776, and in 1788, the United States Constitution.

In order to maintain control of their new land, the invaders organized a government. It was structured to provide freedom for all those who came ashore. With this basic principal in mind, they forged forward.

The Declaration of Independence describes the rights of all people. It states that all men are born equal; that is, they all have the same rights. It also says that government exists to protect each citizen's right to life, liberty, and happiness.

The Constitution sets out a federal system of government. This means that there is a national (federal) government and state governments. The United States is a republic. It has a president, elected by the people; a congress to make the laws; and a Supreme Court, the highest court in the land.

In 1789, the people elected their first president, George Washington. In order to unite the new country under his leadership, Washington signed treaties with England, Spain, and the Native Americans.

Treaties and agreements with the American government began to give the Native Americans annuities and supplies, mostly in exchange for land ownership.

CHAPTER FOUR

Cherokee Go West of

Mississippi River

Standing on the bank of the Tennessee River, the Cherokee Chief Bowles spoke with authority to his people.

"The deed is done. Right or wrong, I find myself in disfavor of my people. There will be no justice from the white man. You have chosen to place the blame on me alone. I carry that burden.

I must leave this place. With those who choose to go with me, we must seek a new land. Let us follow the river till we reach the mighty one, which we will cross and make a home where we can preserve what remains of our traditional culture."

***

ONE LEGEND TOLD

In 1794, some white immigrants were on their way down the Tennessee River in a boat carrying goods that they wanted to trade to the Indians. After hearing that the Cherokee had real money, the white men invited the Indians on board the boat. They gave the Indians as much whiskey as they could drink. The whole time, the white men planned to take advantage of the Indians after they got drunk.

The Indians, led by Cherokee Chief Bowles, bought items at very high prices. They did not stop trading until their money was all gone.

After sobering up, Bowles and his men realized that the white men had duped them. Bowles returned the white man's merchandise and tried to get the Indians' money back. The white men ordered him off the boat.

His warriors called for immediate revenge, but Chief Bowles wanted to settle the matter peacefully. Taking two warriors, he tried again, warning the traders that the Indians would fight if the money were not returned. The white men attacked the three Indians, killing one. Bowles escaped but soon returned and killed the remaining white men on the boat. He did not harm the women and children.

***

SECOND LEGEND TOLD

In 1794, when Duwa'li Bowles was chief of the Cherokee of Running Water, Tennessee, the American government had begun to give the Indians annuities and supplies. Chief Bowles and a small group of Indians went to the government post to pick up their allotments. On their way home, they met some white traders with their families. The white men traded some whiskey to the Indians, and the Indians got drunk. The traders then proceeded to bargain for all of the supplies, giving very little to the Indians in return. After becoming sober, the Indians realized what had happened and asked the white traders to return their supplies, but they refused.

A battle ensued in which all of the white traders were killed. The Indians took the white women and children to safety.

If either legend were true, it was sure to be called a massacre by the whites. Chief Bowles knew that it would be fruitless to defend his actions; retaliation was certain. He decided to lead his tribe to a new home, a search that spanned half the continent.

Chief Bowles's decision to lead his people west, across the Mississippi River, turned out to be ironic because it fell right into line with the plans of the Europeans' newly formed government. As early as 1776, Thomas Jefferson, a statesman who later became president of the American government, recommended removing the Indians to lands west of the Mississippi River.

"Indian removal," said Jefferson "was the only way to ensure the survival of Native American peoples." This was his justification for taking control of the land that the Native Americans inhabited.

His original plan was to coerce the Indians to give up their own cultures, religions, and lifestyles in favor of Western European culture.

In order to maintain control of their new land, the European settlers expected to assimilate the natives into a market- based agricultural society and strip them of their self-sufficiency. The Indians would become economically dependent on trade with white Americans, and would therefore be willing to give up land that they would not part with otherwise in exchange for trade goods or to pay debts.

Jefferson believed his strategy would get rid of the pesky Indians without offending them. In cases where native tribes resisted assimilation, he believed that they should be forcefully removed from their land and sent west.

Jefferson revealed his thoughts in two letters. In a private letter to William Henry Harrison in 1803, Jefferson wrote:

To promote this disposition to exchange lands, which they have to spare and we want, for necessaries, which we have to spare and they want, we shall push our trading uses, and be glad to see the good and influential individuals among them run in debt, because we observe that when these debts get beyond what the individuals can pay, they become willing to lop them off by a cession of lands... In this way our settlements will gradually circumscribe and approach the Indians, and they will in time either incorporate with us as citizens of the United States, or remove beyond the Mississippi. The former is certainly the termination of their history most happy for themselves; but, in the whole course of this, it is essential to cultivate their love. As to their fear, we presume that our strength and their weakness is now so visible that they must see we have only to shut our hand to crush them and that all our liberalities to them proceed from motives of pure humanity only. Should any tribe be fool hardy enough to take up the hatchet at any time, the seizing of the whole country of that tribe, and driving them across the Mississippi as the only condition of peace, would be an example to others, and a furtherance of our final consolidation.

In 1813, Thomas Jefferson wrote to Alexander Van Humboldt:

You know, my friend, the benevolent plan we were pursuing here for the happiness of the aboriginal inhabitants in our vicinities. We spared nothing to keep them at peace with one another. To teach them agriculture and the rudiments of the most necessary arts, and to encourage industry by establishing among them separate property. In this way they would have been enabled to blood with ours and been amalgamated and identified with us within no distant period of time. On the commencement of our present war, we pressed on them the observance of peace and neutrality, but the interested and unprincipled policy of England has defeated all our labors for the salvation of these unfortunate people. They have seduced the greater part of the tribes within our neighborhood, to take up the hatchet against us, and the cruel massacres they have committed on the women and children of our frontiers taken by surprise, will oblige us now to pursue them to extermination, or drive them to new seats beyond our reach.

With the ever-increasing number of white American settlers and a need for a place to put the Indians who were to

32

be removed from their present homelands, Thomas Jefferson, president of the American government, looked west.

West of the Mississippi River was a territory owned by France. In 1799, this territory, then under the control of Spain, was given to the French in exchange for the promise of a throne in central Italy. Although the agreement was signed on October 1, 1800, it did not go into effect until 1802. The following year, Napoleon, the leader of France, sold Louisiana to the United States.

The borders of this Louisiana Territory were not explicitly specified, and the descriptions in the documents were ambiguous and contradictory. Jefferson claimed that the territory stretched west to the Rocky Mountains and included the entire watershed of the Mississippi and Missouri Rivers and their tributaries, and that the southern border was the Rio Grande. Boundaries in Texas were questionable, but Texas was considered a buffer province between Spain and the United States.

In 1804, President Jefferson sent two army officers, Meriwether Lewis and William Clark, to explore this vast area. Their instructions were to find the source of the Missouri River, to reach the Pacific Ocean, and to report on the Indians they met there and on the natural history of the land itself.

Lewis and Clark reached the Pacific Ocean in November 1805. Their eighteen-month journey had taken them nearly 4,000 miles (6,400 kilometers).

As a result of their expedition, the territory now owned by the United States was opened up to increased migration of the white American settlers from the East.

Chief Bowles and his band of Cherokee Indians had settled in Southeastern Missouri, in the Saint Francis River valley, near New Madrid, Missouri.

The chief and his people were content on their new land.

The hunting grounds were good, and it seemed as though they had escaped the growing pressure of white American settlers.

All were peaceful save one. They called him Sky Walker.

CHAPTER FIVE

Sky Walker/Texas

"What is on the other side of the sky?" asked the eleven-year- old brother of Chief Bowles. As was Chief Bowles, the boy was the son of a Scottish father and full-blooded Cherokee mother. They had lived in the Great Smoky Mountains of western North Carolina and then in the valley of eastern Tennessee before Chief Bowles led his band of Cherokee west, across the Mississippi River.

"Why are we always following your little brother?" asked the men of the village.

"Because," Chief Bowles explained, "he is looking for the other side of the sky, and if he finds it, we will all prosper. And because he is my little brother."

Calling him "Sky Walker," the people of the village tolerated his behavior, and some were willing to follow him in his search for a place on the other side of the sky.

Restless with all the boundaries he had explored, at age twenty, Sky Walker said good-bye to his brother. Leaving to follow the setting sun, he and a small band of Cherokee traveled west, beyond Missouri. If the other side of the sky were to be found, they would surely do so.

He and his band of Cherokee traveled slowly and deliberately, each day straining to see what lay before them. As they searched the western horizon, Sky Walker's vision of a place on the other side of the sky seemed to fade.

On the sunny and pleasant morning of December 29, 1807, the wayward tribe awakened to a world that dreams are made of.

In front of them and stretching for miles beyond their sight, a river flowed gently, creasing the land with low banks of green grass and pine tree forest.

What unseen hand had guided Sky Walker to

this place?

He did not know, nor would he question it.

Entering the valley, he felt serene, free, and confident that his journey was over. Sky Walker told his people, "Upon this land we shall work unhampered by any other ties. Our ideals are to be vested in our love for each other and the land."

Along the banks of the Red River, Sky Walker and his followers set about creating a village.

Waking at daybreak, putting on his moccasins, and stepping down to the water's edge, Sky Walker splashed handfuls of clear, cold water onto his face. As the dawn advanced, he stood, facing the sun as it danced upon the horizon. In the new, sweet earth around him, he felt the presence of his ancestors. To the spirits of the Cherokee, he offered an unspoken prayer. Thank you for all that I have and all that I am.

As they worked together, their settlement began to take shape. Indian tribes, such as the Caddo and Osage, were no strangers to this land. But the Cherokee were different. They built and lived in log cabins, farmed the land, and raised livestock.

Before the Cherokee crossed the Mississippi

River, they had adopted many European ways. The European teachings made many changes in the Cherokee way of life, such as in the tools they used, their dress, and some customs.

All the things they had learned would be helpful, as this band of Cherokee would soon to find out. They were not isolated on their land along the Red River.

Sky Walker and his people were just another community living in territory already dominated by Europeans. The Red River Valley was connected to a place called Texas.

TEXAS

Before 1500 CE, five million to ten million Indians lived in North America. Most were nomadic or seminomadic; tribes were sedentary only where there was intense agriculture. They were hunter-gatherers and practiced agriculture and aquaculture only in fairer climates.

Their lives harmonized with nature. Epidemic diseases were unknown. The hardships came in dealing with what nature imposed and in the daily tasks of providing for their material needs.

During the 1500s, the ancestral homeland of Native American tribes changed forever. Across the seas came the Europeans. First to arrive in the region now known as Texas were the Spanish conquistadors.

In 1519, the Spaniard Alvarez de Pineda created the first map of the northern Gulf Coast. This map is the earliest document of Texas history.

The Spanish were searching for a passage between the Gulf of Mexico and Asia, and they were on a quest for gold. Finding neither the passage nor the gold in the area now known as Texas, the Spanish essentially ignored it for over 160 years.

In 1682, a French nobleman, Rene-Robert Cavalier, Sieur de La Salle, claimed the entire Mississippi River Valley for France. When the Spanish learned of French settlements, they launched expeditions to secure their authority over the land.

On January 23, 1691, Spain appointed the first governor of Texas, General Domingo Teran de los Rios. For the next one hundred years, wars ensued between Spain and France and between Spain and Native American Indian tribes. In 1799, Spain gave the area known as Louisiana to France. Then, in 1803, France sold the territory to the United States.

Spain and the United States disagreed on the territory borders. Spain claimed the area known as Texas and considered it a buffer province between New Spain in America and the United States.

In 1807, the Cherokee entered the Red River Valley of Texas.

CHAPTER SIX

Earthquake 1811-1812

As Sky Walker and Bright Flower began their life together in the Red River Valley of Texas, Chief Bowles's future was uncertain. When Sky Walker walked west to follow his dream, Chief Bowles and his people had stayed in the valley of the Saint Francis River in southeast Missouri. They remained there for eighteen years. During their stay, their numbers increased, and the entire area became known as the Cherokee Nation West.

Their peaceful life ended on December 11, 1811. Houses trembled; the ground shook and sank in many places. Rivers rolled and bolted as never before. Striking the Cherokee lands was a violent earthquake—a quake more powerful than any remembered by the elders.

Surely, it was the work of the Great Spirit. Frightened that the Great Spirit was perhaps warning them that they should not be living in this part of the country, Chief Bowles and the Cherokee people moved.

Their new settlement was the territory between the Arkansas and White Rivers in present-day Arkansas. Other Cherokee began to emigrate to Arkansas, and by 1813, approximately one third of the Cherokee were living west of the Mississippi River.

The year 1813 was a time of change for Chief Bowles and his people in Arkansas, as well as for Sky Walker.

Historical Facts

- **Cherokee Wedding**: The ceremony differs from clan to clan and community to community, but they all use the same basic rituals. Clanship is matrilineal in the Cherokee society. It is forbidden to marry within one's own clan. The woman holds the family clan.

- **Cherokee Wedding Vase**: The vessel holds one drink but has two openings so the couple may drink at the same time.

- **Cherokee Nation Marriage Law**: Cherokee couples are allowed to marry under this law instead of the state marriage laws because the Cherokee Nation is a sovereign nation. The couple is not required to obtain a license; however, the Cherokee Nation must license the person conducting the ceremony. A certificate is signed by the couple and the religious leader and then given to the Cherokee Nation District Court for the official records.

- **Cherokee in the Beginning**: The prehistoric origin of the Cherokee is shrouded in mystery. We know that their language is Iroquoian, an Indian tribe of North America. When Europeans came to America, they found the Cherokee inhabiting a large area of the south Allegheny Mountains. They lived as farmers and hunters. Sixty percent of the world's food supply comes from crops first cultivated by Native Americans. Some of these crops are potatoes, beans, corn, peanuts, pumpkins, tomatoes, squash, and melons.

- **United States**: The land that is now the United States was first settled thousands of years ago by the ancestors of the American Indians. European settlements began after Christopher Columbus made his first voyage to the New World in 1492. The British, French, Spanish, and other Europeans fought for control of the land. The

British succeeded, but their American colonies revolted and declared their independence as the United States of America on July 4, 1776.

- **Declaration of Independence**: This document marked the birth of the United States. It proclaimed that the thirteen British colonies in North America were no longer under British rule. It also stated that although they were independent states, they were also united. The rights of each citizen were declared, and the government existed to protect those rights. Written on parchment, the Declaration of Independence can be seen in the National Archives building in Washington, DC.

- **Constitution of the United States**: Written in 1787 and ratified by all states by 1790, it is the supreme law of the land. This document sets out a federal system of government, a national government, and state governments. The Constitution states that the United States is a republic. It has a president elected by the people. There is also a Congress to make the laws, and a Supreme Court, the highest court in the land. The Constitution is on display in the National Archives in Washington, DC.

- **President of the United States**: The executive power is vested in a president of the United States of America. The president is the leader of the states, the chief executive officer of the government, and the commander in chief of the armed forces.

- **George Washington**: The first president of the United States. He was born on February 12, 1732, in Westmoreland County, Virginia. His term of office was 1789–1797. He died on December 14, 1799, at Mount Vernon, Virginia.

- **John Adams**: The first vice president of the United States and the second president. He was born on October 30, 1735, in Braintree, Massachusetts. He was president from 1797 to 1801. He died on July 4, 1826, in Quincy, Massachusetts.

- **Thomas Jefferson**: Third president of the United States. He was born on April 13, 1743, in Shadwell, Virginia. His term of office was 1801–1809. He died on July 4, 1826, at Monticello, Virginia.

- **Interesting Note**: John Adams and Thomas Jefferson died on the same day, July 4, 1826, fifty years after signing the Declaration of Independence.

- **Louisiana Purchase**: In 1803, the United States purchased the Louisiana Territory from France. This territory had an area of 828,000 square miles (2,144,500 kilometers). It stretched from the Mississippi River in the east to the Rocky Mountains in the west, and from the Gulf of Mexico in the south to British North America in the north. Eventually, all or parts of fifteen states were formed from the Louisiana Territory. At the time, the Louisiana Purchase doubled the size of the United States.

- **Lewis and Clark Expedition**: Until this expedition in 1804 through 1806, much of the area of the Louisiana Purchase was unexplored. Under the orders of President Thomas Jefferson, two army officers, Meriwether Lewis and William Clark, with a party of forty-four, set off from Saint Louis, Missouri, in May 1804. Their route along the Missouri River took them as far north as present- day Bismarck, North Dakota. There, they built a fort and enlisted the aid of a French-Canadian trapper and his Indian wife, Sacagawea, as guides and interpreters. Heading west, the expedition crossed the Rockies and traveled down the Columbia River to the Pacific Ocean. On the way, the explorers established friendly relations with several Indian tribes and collected plant and mineral specimens. They returned to Saint Louis in September 1806.

- **Chief Bowles**: Cherokee Indian Chief Bowles, also known as Duwa'li, was born in North Carolina around 1756. He was the son of a Scottish father and a full-blooded Cherokee mother. He moved his band of Cherokee across the Mississippi River and settled in the Saint Francis River valley, near New Madrid, Missouri. In 1812–1813, the group moved into northwestern Arkansas, south of the Arkansas River, and then into Texas in 1819.

- **Texas**: The word derives from *ta ysha*, a word in the Caddoan language of the Hasinai, which means "friends" or "allies." Between 1519 and 1848, all of Texas or parts of it were claimed by six countries: France, Spain, Mexico, the Republic of Texas, the United States of America, and the Confederate States.

- **Red River Valley**: A land held dear by who live there. The allure of the Red River beckoned the Native Americans to a peaceful place they could call home. Native Americans called the river the "Rio Colorado," or Red River, because of the water's red appearance due to the "red beds" land in the watershed. Extending along the northern border of Texas and the southern border of Oklahoma, the river and its fertile valley support abundant life. Many expeditions in search of happiness and a place to call home ended in sorrow.

- **The Song, "Red River Valley":** Sometime before 1896, a song was written that expresses the sorrow of a local woman as her soldier lover prepared to return to Ontario or a local man whose girlfriend or wife could not take the harsh life in Texas and left him to return to Canada. This song has captured the emotions of people all around the world and down through generations. Is it because of this special place we call the Red River Valley or is it inspired by our longing for love and a place to call home? The song has been given various names, and its origins are controversial. Below is the song as arranged and adapted by Arlo Guthrie:

Red River Valley
From this valley they say you are going
We will miss your bright eyes and sweet smile
For they say you are taking my sunshine
That has brightened our pathways awhile.

CHORUS

Come and sit by my side, if you love me

Do not hasten to bid me adieu

Just remember the Red River Valley

And the cowboy who loved you so there.

I've been thinking a long time, my darling

Of the sweet words you never would say

Now, alas, must my fond hopes all vanish

For they say you are going away

Do you think of the valley you're leaving

O how lovely and how dreary it will be

And do you think of the kind hearts you're breaking

And the pain you are causing to me.

CHORUS

They will bury me where you have wandered

Near the hills where the daffodils grow

When you're gone from the Red River Valley

For I can't live without you, I know.

CHAPTER SEVEN

Baby Eagle

With the wind rising, the western sky filled with streaks from the setting sun, ending a warm summer day.

At river's edge, Bright Flower knelt to fill her water jar. In the distance, an eagle called. Its call grew louder as it soared closer, above the flowing water.

The Indian woman stood still as the majestic bird ended it flight, resting on a tree branch at river's edge. These two had met many times before, sharing the beauty of the Red River Valley.

The eagle watched as she said a prayer. "I pray my child will be as free as the eagle. Time has come for you to enter this world. I do not know where your journey will take you. I pray the flight of the eagle will show you the path to take."

The breeze grew gentle, and then the air was still. Bright Flower turned to walk home. The eagle disappeared into the twilight.

In the summer of 1813, a baby boy was born. Bright Flower and Sky Walker named him Little Eagle.

All of the villagers rejoiced and took pleasure in tending to the child. Everyone worked together to have a peaceful life and a place they could call home along the banks of the Red River.

One moment in time can change everything, however, as this Cherokee village would soon discover.

Hanging low over the valley, the morning fog hid the approaching danger. A volley of arrows awoke those who were still sleeping. Indians (Osage) raced through the village, cutting down those in their path and setting fire to houses.

Sky Walker leaped into action along with the other warriors of the village. It was man-to-man combat. Women screamed desperately, and children cried.

Brave fighting by the Cherokee warriors spared most of the women and children and kept the village from burning.

Fighting their enemy back across the river, the Cherokee knew who they were. They did not know the reason for the attack, only that the Osage Indian was their enemy.

Bathed in fright, Little Eagle, now three years old, waited for the footsteps of his father on the porch. Listening, Little Eagle heard the footsteps that his mother, lying dead beside her bed, did not. Sky Walker called her name as he entered the cabin and cradled his son in his arms.

Still grasping the hatchet that was almost as big as he was, Little Eagle cried, "Father, I hit the bad man as hard as I could."

"You are my brave warrior," Sky Walker said. He moved to the door to see Bright Flower's mother running toward them.

Sky Walker would seek revenge for the death of his beloved Bright Flower; all his life, Little Eagle would remember the time when he listened for the footsteps and his father's words, "You are my brave warrior."

Women prepared food for the men; they parched corn and pounded it into meal. They gave a bagful to each warrior. The Cherokee warriors would travel as many days as it took to seek out the ones who had attacked their village.

Sky Walker left his son standing beside his grandmother.

He said to Bright Flower's mother, "If I do not return, tell my son I will meet him on the other side of the sky.

CHAPTER EIGHT

Grandmother/Growing Boy

Celebration, especially since Bright Flower and Sky Walker had been married for four years without a child.

Going into the wilderness alone, where no curious or pitying eyes would embarrass her, Bright Flower give birth to her child. A pair of eyes opened upon her; she felt the endearing warmth and heard the soft breathing. Nothing was sweeter than the deep, trusting gaze of the child she had created was.

Presently, Bright Flower returned to the village carrying the dear bundle.

Sky Walker, having made a cradle ready, held his son briefly before placing him there. Grandmother, other family members, and people of the village all gathered to see the newborn.

After a time, loud cries came from the baby. He was more than just fretful. He seemed to say, "Enough is enough. Leave me alone. I'm hungry."

Sky Walker called out, "Little Eagle has spoken.

Everyone must leave him alone. He wants only his mother."

The baby's demand was met, and it was only his first, as Little Eagle would realize that by making a loud noise, people would do as he demanded.

Not so with Grandmother. After the death of his mother and during the absence of his father, Little Eagle was raised by his grandmother.

Grandmother showed no less enthusiasm for Little Eagle than she had shown when she held her firstborn, the boy's mother, in her arms. Every little attention that was due a growing child, she performed with much skill and devotion.

Little Eagle had outgrown his cradle and was old enough to follow Grandmother about her tasks. She began calling his attention to natural objects. Whenever they heard the song of a bird, she would tell him what bird the sound came from. Saying, "My child, listen to *sshechoka* (the robin) calling his mate. He says he has just found something good to eat." Or, "Listen to *oopehanska* (the thrush); he is singing for his little wife. He will sing his best."

Grandmother trained the boy to go to sleep, as she said, with the birds, and to awaken with them. She told him an Indian must always rise early. In the first place, she said, a hunter finds his game best at daybreak. Secondly, other tribes, when on the warpath, usually attack very early in the morning, as was the case when the Osage attacked their village, killing Little Eagle's mother.

Since Little Eagle already had the habit of making loud demands, instilling in the little boy the need to be silent and slow to speak was quite a challenge for Grandmother. Considering that it was one of the most important traits to form in the character of the Indian, Grandmother was relentless in her teaching. Although she understood that there were times when boisterous actions were necessary, it was not the Cherokee habit. She was determined to lay the foundation of patience and self-control.

For Little Eagle, Grandmother's teachings were interesting. He was beginning to learn of life's realities.

He formed habits that served him well as a hunter and as a warrior. The spirit of daring and courage was no longer just a whisper.

CHAPTER NINE

Chief Bowles Moves to Texas

Grandmother told Little Eagle stories of his father's brother. "Your uncle is the great Chief Bowles," Grandmother said. "He led our people across the mighty river they call Mississippi.

"When your father, Sky Walker, left Chief Bowles and many of our people, I followed your father to this place. I believed in your father's dream of finding the other side of the sky.

"When we left our people and Chief Bowles in their newfound home in Missouri, they were content," she said. "We heard that the land cracked beneath Chief Bowles's feet, so he had to move our people again."

Believing the earthquake to be an omen warning them to leave that piece of land, Chief Bowles relocated his band of Cherokee in Arkansas.

Only a few years passed before misfortunate befell the Cherokee again. This time, it came in the guise of a team of surveyors. Chief Bowles was told that he and his people had settled on the wrong side of the Arkansas River. Their settlement was not on the land ceded to the Indians by the US government. They were ordered to move.

Angered at being told to move and anxious to escape the jurisdiction of the United States, Chief Bowles took sixty families with him and moved all the way to Texas. The autumn-colored leaves were still bright on the trees when they arrived in the Red River Valley. The year was 1820.

Their new homeland was located on the Three Forks of the Trinity River (on the site of present-day Dallas). The area was much like their old lands to the east, with tall pines, rolling hills, and clear streams. But this good fortune did not last.

Pressure from prairie tribes forced them to move eastward into a virtually uninhabited region north of Nacogdoches, Texas.

This land previously had been occupied by the

Caddoes, a once powerful Indian confederacy that had been greatly reduced by warfare and epidemic diseases.

With strength and endurance, the Cherokee were able to carve out farms on this land. By 1822, the Texas Cherokee population had grown to nearly three hundred.

Upon arriving in Texas, Chief Bowles knew that he must secure a single piece of paper that would grant his people legal rights to their settlement.

The territory was governed by the Spanish, to whom Chief Bowles made his first request. But before the Spanish could issue a grant to the Cherokee, the government of Texas passed from Spain to Mexico.

Mexican officials, like their Spanish predecessors, welcomed the presence of Cherokee in Texas. Their policy was to use the Cherokee as a buffer against immigrants from the United States.

However, it would be several years before Mexico considered giving the Cherokee title to their land.

Upon entering the Red River Valley, Chief Bowles asked about his brother, Sky Walker. He was told about the hostile Indian attack on the village in which Sky Walker's wife was killed and about Sky Walker's departure to avenge her death.

Six years had passed with no word on Sky Walker. No doubt, he was dead or he would have returned to care for his son. The boy was being raised by his grandmother.

Immediately upon hearing this, Chief Bowles gave an order. "Bring to me the grandmother and my nephew."

CHAPTER TEN

Uncle Bowles Meets Little Eagle

Out of the morning mist walked a young boy carrying his bow and arrows; not far behind him was Grandmother. They had come to see Chief Bowles.

The chief, sixty-six years old, stood and opened his arms to welcome his nephew. Not yielding to an emotional embrace, Little Eagle raised his hand in the traditional Indian greeting. "He is independent," noted the uncle, as he proceeded to ask, "Who is this that stands before me?" He knew the answer, but he wanted to hear the boy speak.

"I am Little Eagle, son of Sky Walker. If you are my uncle, tell me, does my father live on the other side of the sky?"

Being a wise chief, the answer to his nephew came quickly. "If there is such a place, I am sure your father found it. As far as my being your uncle, if your grandmother told you this, then it is true."

A meal was prepared, and the visit lasted until the sun hid behind the western hills.

"The winter wind is cold. You and Grandmother will stay in this village until the snow falls no more," Chief Bowles said, making it clear that the two would live with him at least until spring.

But Grandmother would not live to see the grass turn green. The harsh winter of 1822 took her life. She left her beloved grandson, believing she would join his father on the other side of the sky.

As springtime brought new growth to the earth, Chief Bowles had guided Little Eagle through the grieving process over the loss of his grandmother. They spent many hours walking through the woods or sitting at the creek's edge. The foundation for the person this young boy would become was being created.

Grandmother had been wise and protective and taught the boy many skills, but the boy was nine years old and ready for training that was more Spartan.

"Your father, my brother Sky Walker, was a good warrior; you will be a great warrior," Chief Bowles said, beginning his lessons.

"You must always remember not all heroes come from man killing man; some come from other struggles.

"At your young age, you have already proven to me your sense of independence and strength of character. Therefore, from henceforth, you will no longer be called Little Eagle. You shall be called War Eagle."

Little Eagle Becomes War Eagle

"Sometimes Uncle Bowles is just a funny old man," War Eagle told his friends. "Other times, he can be strict with my discipline. But he is a good teacher."

Throughout the day, War Eagle knew he must be observant of his natural surroundings, because when the sun set, Uncle Bowles would question him. "On which side of the tree is the lighter-colored bark? On which side does the tree have most regular branches?"

The best questions were those about birds. "Can you name all the birds you saw today?"

The surprise came when War Eagle not only named the birds, but also identified them according to their colors, the shapes of their bills, their songs, and the appearance and location of their nests.

Surprised but smiling warmly, the chief never

questioned the source of War Eagle's knowledge. War Eagle never told him that it was Grandmother who had taught him about birds.

Fishing was a skill where War Eagle had been left on his own. With Uncle Bowles, he learned the art of fishing.

"Survey the waters," he said. "The fish will jump out of the water for flies at midday. Little pebbles grouped together under the shallow water and curved marks with little sand banks in the river bottom are clues to finding fish. Watch the fish-eating birds carefully; they will show you where to find fish."

When War Eagle was older, Chief Bowles asked, "What do you do with that bow and arrows you have?"

"Mostly hunt rabbits," replied War Eagle.

"If you want to be a great hunter," the Chief said, "you will be guided by the habits of the animal you seek. You must always take a second look at everything you see.

"Follow the example of the wolf," he continued. "Even when he is surprised and runs for his life, he will pause to take one more look at you before he enters his final retreat."

"Uncle," War Eagle interrupted. "What will I do if a bear or a wild-cat comes after me?"

"Don't be afraid," Chief Bowles said, instilling

confidence. "If the creature shows signs of attacking you, you must make him fully understand that you have seen him and are aware of his intentions. The cat or bear is generally afraid of the common weapon of another animal. He dares not risk an open attack if you have a long, sharp-pointed pole and use it as a spear to rush toward him.

"Of course, you can use your bow and arrow," he said. "In the spring, we will test your bow and arrow skills."

***

Early one morning, uncle and nephew concealed themselves in a convenient place. They observed signs of the presence of a doe and her fawn.

Stepping back, Chief Bowles motioned for War Eagle to take the lead. Spotting the deer, War Eagle readied his bow and arrow. After brushing the feathered end of the arrow against his lips, he placed it in the bow, against the taut string. He hesitated for a moment, and then let go. The arrow sailed straight ahead.

In a flash, the doe looked up, flinched, and with her fawn close to her side, disappeared into the underbrush.

The thing that made this scene ridiculously funny, leaving Chief Bowles and War Eagle lying on the grass laughing, was that just before War Eagle let go of the arrow, he let out a loud yell, like a war chant.

"My nephew," said Chief Bowles, recovering from his laughter. "You are trying to catch dinner, not ring the dinner bell."

"Uncle," War Eagle explained, "it won't be funny when you find the doe dead. I believe my arrow struck her."

Shaking his head, the Chief replied, "Should the deer be dead in yonder thicket, it will be because you scared her to death with that loud yelling."

At the end of the day, uncle and nephew walked back to their village with a couple of rabbits for dinner, but lessons were learned.

After the first hunt together, Chief Bowles began to give war whoops over the head of War Eagle in the morning when he was still asleep. Since War Eagle knew the blood-curdling yells, it was time for him to learn to be a warrior.

If War Eagle aspired to be a great warrior, Chief Bowles said, he must not refuse to do any of the tasks that his uncle gives him. He was expected to endure hardship without complaint.

Chief Bowles had War Eagle go without food and water for two to three days and run for a day and a night without rest. He learned to traverse pathless and wild country without losing his way, both in the daylight and at night.

War Eagle excelled as an athlete and at enduring all sorts of hardships. But he needed a lot of practice at remaining unafraid.

Camping in a strange place, Uncle Bowles sent his nephew to get water after dark. Picking his way through the woods, War Eagle dipped his pail in the water and hurried back, always careful to make as little noise as a cat would make.

Every crackling of a dry twig or distant hooting of an owl made his heart skip a beat. After all, there could be wild beasts or hostile Indians waiting to attack.

Just as he was being brave and emptying the contents of the pail before his uncle, Chief Bowles said, "You are a good warrior. Now you can go a second time."

War Eagle never objected because that would mean he was a coward. Along with all of this hunting, fishing, and warrior training, not to be neglected were his education and manners.

Grandmother, although she could not read or write, had known Indian etiquette well. Strict with her teaching, she had wasted no time in training her grandson. He was made to respect adults, especially the aged; to be generous to the poor; and always to give reverence to the Great Spirit.

Many times, Grandmother had warned the Cherokee lad that a soft, low, voice was an excellent thing. He must be strong of heart along with being patient. It was most necessary to control his voice and his temper. Failure to do so would lead to bad consequences, she had said.

Grandmother had told War Eagle of a young chief who was noted for his uncontrollable temper. While in one of his rages, he attempted to kill a woman. For that crime, his own tribe slew him. He was left unburied as a mark of disgrace—his body was simply covered with green grass.

Teaching the boy a lesson, Grandmother had said, "Little Eagle, control yourself or you will be like the young chief I tell you of and lie under a green blanket!"

When War Eagle asked his Uncle Bowles about this story, Chief Bowles confirmed wholeheartedly, "It's true!"

Knowing that his nephew's morals and manners had not been neglected, Chief Bowles could now begin to educate the young Cherokee.

For this task, he called upon one of his daughters. This daughter of Chief Bowles had married the son of Sequoyah. Sequoyah had joined Bowles's tribe in Arkansas, and it was there that Sequoyah diligently devised the Cherokee syllabary.

Sequoyah did not go with Bowles into Texas. He

returned to the Cherokee nation in the Eastern United States and introduced literacy to his people.

Chief Bowles's daughter had mastered Sequoyah's Cherokee alphabet and was an excellent teacher. She not only taught War Eagle the Cherokee written language, but she taught him the written and spoken language of the white American people too.

By the age of fifteen, War Eagle was envied by many of his friends. He was an excellent hunter, a noted warrior, and an educated young man.

Competing in games and sports, War Eagle was always the favorite to win. The competition was keen, with each player striving to beat all the others.

In wrestling, often a much stronger opponent would vanquish War Eagle. A great many boys played this game. It was a battle in which each one chose his opponent. No striking with the hands was permitted, but all manner of tripping with legs and feet and butting with knees were allowed. It was an exhausting game, equal to the American game of football, and only the strongest athlete was left standing.

Needless to say, War Eagle was not fond of wrestling. Other games that he fully enjoyed were feats with the bow and arrow, foot and pony races, swimming, fights with mud balls and willow wands, and playing lacrosse.

Making war upon a nest of wild bees was the best time of all. Imagining they were about to attack an enemy tribe, each painted himself in the Cherokee warrior tradition. They approached the bees' nest cautiously, and then, with a rush and war whoops, they sprang upon the target and endeavored to destroy it.

But it seemed that the bees were always on the alert and never entirely surprised, for they always raised as many scalps as the bold assailants did!

Even so, after the onslaught upon the nest, they staged a pretend scalp dance. There didn't seem to be a clear winner in this game.

Whether in lessons with his Uncle Bowles or at games with his friends, War Eagle found nothing that set the days apart; they all were good.

He was blessed with a home. Humble in his gratitude, he often paused for an instant in the attitude of worship. For only the Great Spirit could give him a life filled with such striking beauty—a black thundercloud with the rainbow's glowing arch above the mountains, a white waterfall in the heart of a green gorge, a vast prairie tinged with the red of sunset. All this and the enduring love of family formed the essence of War Eagle.

PART TWO

CHAPTER ELEVEN

Sam Houston Comes to Texas

Red River Valley, where the four winds met and where the waters flowed freely, was home. When silence of the night met the rising orange glow of sunlight, all were blessed with the sight and experience of another day.

The ground upon which he walked, this place of beauty and peace, War Eagle called home.

First with a murmur, then a whisper, and then loud talk of recognition, the Cherokee men, women, and children escorted him. Riding a stunning white horse, he graciously acknowledged the warm welcome as he rode into the Cherokee village of Caney Creek. He was the biggest white man War Eagle had ever seen. He was Sam Houston.

"What brings you to Texas?" Chief Bowles asked as he greeted his friend.

At the end of the day, it was War Eagle asking all the questions. "Uncle, is that man our enemy? What about the young guy? Is he Cherokee or enemy?"

With a reassuring smile, Chief Bowles explained, "Don't let the color of the man's skin fool you, for his heart is of the Cherokee.

"We call him the Raven. As for as the young fellow, I believe his name is Little Bear. I am told he came from the old country across the big river, our homeland."

The chief hung his head for a moment, and he then continued the tale. The Raven was named Sam Houston before he lived with the Cherokee. For reasons unknown, he left his white parents when he was just a lad and took shelter with a Cherokee tribe. Chief of the tribe, Chief John Jolly (*Ahuludegi*) adopted the boy, Sam Houston. As Sam grew older, his desire was to return to his Scotch-Irish family. The wise Chief John Jolly encouraged him to follow his heart.

Many years passed as Sam Houston became the builder of a school, a soldier in the 1812 War, a lawyer, a United States congressman, and the governor of the state of Tennessee. After a stormy personal life, he returned to the Cherokee. His adopted father welcomed him with open arms.

Old love and friendship was renewed, but in a different land.

The Cherokee tribe of which Sam Houston, now known as the Raven, was made a member had moved across the big river, west, to a place called Oklahoma. Chief John Jolly was now the chief of the Western Cherokee.

"To answer your question, no, the Raven is not our enemy," Chief Bowles said. "He came to us as a friend, bringing greetings from the great western chief of Oklahoma.

"I do not know the young Cherokee who comes with him, but I know if he is with Sam Houston, he is not our enemy."

"Uncle," War Eagle asked, "have you ever met the great western Cherokee chief you call John Jolly?"

"Yes, I met him several times. He was a mentor in my learning our Cherokee ways. I came to share the same struggle—to maintain our quest for a land we can call home. The lands of our fathers have disappeared into the hands of the white men who invaded our shores," he said. "They have left us searching."

Chief Bowles walked away from War Eagle.

The night was restless, as War Eagle tried to sort out all that he had been told and the arrival of the giant man on his white horse and the young fellow whom Uncle called Little Bear.

War Eagle had only one more question, this one for himself. "I wonder if I will ever see this Sam Houston again. Oh yes, and Little Bear. Will our paths meet again?"

CHAPTER TWELVE

Winds of Change

Leaving the Cherokee village of Caney Creek, Sam Houston traveled fifty miles south to the town of Nacogdoches, Texas. There, he set up a law firm.

Andrew Jackson, the president of the United States, had asked Mr. Houston to go to Texas and straighten out that mess down there. He was referring to the problems between the Mexicans and the Anglo-Americans who had moved into Texas, problems between the Mexicans and the Cherokee Indians, and the forever problem with the Indians and American settlers.

It was a tall order, but Sam Houston was not one to back away from a challenge. His task began the day he left his friend, Chief Bowles, at Caney Creek. "I will get you a clear paper title to your land," he promised the Cherokee chief.

As soon as he said this, Sam gulped. "Just how am I going to do this?" he wondered.

Early on, since the formation of the Texas Cherokee, the tribe had sought to secure legal rights to their settlement in East Texas.

Chief Richard Fields, newly elected chief of the Texas Cherokee, had applied to the Mexican government for a grant to the land on which the tribe was living. He spent a year in Mexico and was joined there by a white man named John Dunn Hunter. Hunter had come to live with the Cherokee and had joined their quest for land rights. But he and Chief Fields failed.

Disappointed, Hunter and Chief Fields hatched a scheme to go to war with the Mexican government. When Chief Bowles refused to take part in this war plan, the Mexican government found out about it. Whether by Bowles or by Mexican soldiers, John Dunn Hunter and Chief Richard Fields were killed. Bowles was given the status of war chief.

With no deed to the land, the Cherokee faced an influx of white settlers moving into Texas from the United States.

The prospect of plenty of farmland for raising cotton and cattle lured Anglo-Americans to Texas. Ever since Mexico won independence from Spain, the Mexican government had welcomed white immigrants. Appease the whites and let them deal with the Indians, they reasoned.

Mexico's first land grant to an Anglo-American went to Stephen F. Austin. Actually, the Spanish had made the original grant to Moses Austin, but Mexico ratified it for Austin's son, Stephen.

Stephen F. Austin believed in governmental authority. He took advantage of a spy in the Mexican army, Peter Ellis Bean.

With the citizens of Mexico revolting against their own government, the Texans took advantage of the lack of oversight and formed the Convention of 1832. Their demands included independent statehood for Texas. They reiterated this demand at the Convention of 1833. Austin was the courier who presented the petition to the Mexican government on behalf of Texans. As a result, Austin found himself in a Mexican jail for two years on suspicion of treason.

Right into this lion's den rode Sam Houston. Keeping his promise to Chief Bowles was not his only challenge. Sam Houston was the preeminent frontiersman and friend of the Indian known as Colon-neh or the Raven; he was an adopted son of the Cherokee and fought to secure a permanent home for the Cherokee.

Sam Houston, Chief Richard Fields, John Dunn Hunter, Stephen F. Austin, Peter Ellis Bean were all men of destiny in the truest sense of the word. Each possessed leadership ability coupled with an unshakable determination to further his cause. Like the five fingers of a fist, these men shaped the course of Texas history in ways none of them imagined or desired.

CHAPTER THIRTEEN
Texas Revolution

"Uncle, Uncle," shouted War Eagle, running across the open field toward Caney Creek.

Chief Bowles sat on the bank, watching the fish swim by and the sun glisten on the water.

He was not startled by the shouts, as War Eagle often called his attention to one thing or another. Chief Bowles raised his hands and calmly replied, "OK, my young warrior, what has you so excited this time?"

Catching his breath, War Eagle stood before his uncle. "I have word that Mr. Sam Houston approaches the village."

"That is good news. We will welcome our friend. Sit with me. We will watch the fish on this day, as it seems you have not come to the creek to catch the fish," the chief said, chuckling.

"Mr. Houston coming is not the only news. It is rumored he brings a paper to give us ownership of our land." War Eagle was so excited he could not stand still.

"Let's hope it is not just a rumor. If it is the truth, I will jump into the creek and swim with our fishes," Bowles jested.

"I will hold you to that, Uncle, and if it be true I will join you and the fishes in the creek."

War Eagle and Chief Bowles laughed together. Then, side by side, they walked to the village to wait for Sam Houston's arrival.

Leaves of golden color fell like rain. Mr. Houston (the Raven), tall in his saddle, rode toward Caney Creek.

The closer he got, the faster the pace of his white stallion. Often in his lifetime, Sam Houston would tell of the moment he handed the lone piece of paper to his friend, Cherokee Chief Bowles, fulfilling his promise to Bowles and his people.

In Texas, the Anglo-Americans had organized a provisional government. Because of Sam Houston's influence with both Texans and Cherokee, he recommended including a pledge to recognize Cherokee claims to the land they lived on in East Texas.

On November 13, 1835, the officers of the Texas provisional government met and unanimously adopted a "Solemn Declaration," which read, in part, as follows:

Be it solemnly decreed, that we...solemnly declare that the Cherokee Indians and their associate bands... have derived their first claims to lands included within the bounds herein after mentioned from the Government of Mexico, from whom we have also derived our rights...

We solemnly declare that we will guarantee to them the peaceful enjoyment of their right to their lands, as we do our own...

We solemnly declare that it is our sincere desire that the Cherokee Indians and their associate bands should remain our friends in peace and war, and if they do so, we pledge the public faith for the support of the foregoing declarations.

That day, War Eagle and Chief Bowles swam with the fishes. But the only way the Cherokee would have legal right to the land was if Texas were freed from Mexican rule. Achieving freedom for Texas and the Cherokee would be the ultimate war.

CHAPTER FOURTEEN

Freedom for Texas

"Someday, the United States will reach from coast to coast— the Atlantic Ocean to the Pacific Ocean," said US President James Monroe, articulating the vision of Anglo-Americans.

By 1834, over 30,000 Anglo-Americans lived in Texas with just 7,800 Mexicans. But Texas was still under the rule of Mexico.

Although Mexico implemented several measures to appease the Anglo-Americans, President Antonio Lopez de Santa Anna transformed the Mexican government from a federalist to a centralist state. This provided an excuse for the Anglo-Americans in Texas to revolt against Mexico.

They also felt that the revolt was necessary to protect their basic rights. These new Texas settlers maintained that Mexico had invited them to move to Texas, and they were determined to enjoy the republican institutions to which they were accustomed in their land, the United States of America.

The unrest of the Anglo-Americans erupted into armed conflict on October 23, 1835, at the Battle of Gonzales, when Texas repelled a Mexican attempt to retake a small cannon. This launched the Texas Revolution, and over the next three months, the Texas forces defeated all Mexican troops in the region.

Many of the Texas settlers believed that with the army's initial string of victories, they had won the conflict with Mexico. This was not the case. Mexican President Antonio Lopez de Santa Anna was determined to quell the unrest, and bloody battles ensued between the American settlers and the pursing Mexican army.

General Santa Anna declared himself supreme dictator of Mexico. His reign of terror began in Mexico. As his army moved toward Texas, he methodically devastated the individuals, families, and communities who opposed him.

Soon, Santa Anna had a well-deserved reputation for counterinsurgency, brutality, and massacres.

Early in 1836, Santa Anna personally led a 6,000-man force toward Texas. From the Mexican interior, two main roads led into Texas. One route was to San Antonio, the other to Goliad.

Forts blocked these approaches: Presidio La Bahia (Nuestra Senora de Loreto Presidio) at Goliad and the Alamo at San Antonio.

The Alamo was actually a mission turned into a fort. The new function of both Goliad and the Alamo was to serve as a frontier picket guard, ready to alert the Texas settlements of an enemy advance.

In February 1836, Santa Anna sent a courier to demand that the Alamo surrender. This was never going to happen. The men who defended the Alamo— William Barret Travis, David Crockett, and James Bowie—vowed they would "never surrender or retreat" and swore to achieve "victory or death."

Santa Anna responded with cannonballs and pounded the walls of the Alamo with artillery. Santa Anna waited for the garrison to surrender.

Holed up inside the fort, the Texans hoped that reinforcements would soon arrive. But none came.

On March 6, 1836, a Sunday morning, Santa Anna's army stormed the Alamo. Texan gunners stood by their artillery. They were no match for the 1,800 Mexican soldiers. Soon the soldiers were past the Texas defensive perimeter. As they halted, reformed, and drove forward, their cannon and rifle fire ripped through the fort.

Abandoning the walls, defenders withdrew to the dim rooms of the long barracks. There, some of the bloodiest hand-to-hand fighting occurred.

Among the first to die was the commander of the fort, William Travis. James Bowie, too ravaged by illness to rise from his bed, found no pity. Mexican soldiers slaughtered him with their bayonets.

The chapel fell last. By evening, every Alamo fighting man lay dead. With this victory, Santa Anna marched his army forward to Gonzales, Texas. On March 27, 1936, he captured the second fort, Goliad. Once again, Santa Anna ordered all prisoners to be massacred.

Defeating the Texas garrisons at the Alamo on March 6 and in the battle of Goliad three weeks later, Santa Anna marched into south central and eastern parts of the Texas territory, treating all who took up arms against him as pirates unworthy of mercy.

Fleeing the murderous onslaught, settlers panicked. Across the countryside, they formed refugee trains. Their greatest fear was that the Mexican army would crush their fledgling Texan nation.

Only one obstacle lay in Santa Anna's path to complete victory in Texas: one very large man called Sam Houston.

From the day he entered Texas, Sam Houston was politically involved. He speculated that the United States might annex Texas, but first Texas had to declare independence from Mexico. In November 1835, the already organized Texas army commissioned Houston as major general. Then, at the convention to declare Texan independence in March 1836, he was made commander-in-chief.

General Houston was under no delusions. If Texas independence was to be won, General Santa Anna and his Mexican army had to be defeated. Many people opposed his strategy to accomplish this.

As early as January 17, 1836, Houston had ordered the Alamo abandoned. His request to Governor Henry Smith was:

"I have ordered the fortifications in the town of Bexar, the Alamo location, to be demolished, and if you should think well of it, I will remove all the cannons and other munitions of war to Gonzales, location of Goliad, blow up the Alamo and abandon the place, as it will be impossible to keep up the station with volunteers, the sooner I can be authorized the better it will be for the country."

Governor Smith did not "think well of it" and refused to authorize Houston's proposal. On March 6, Santa Anna forces captured the Alamo. Sam Houston arrived in the town of Gonzales in early March. Upon hearing the news of the fall of the Alamo and reports of fleeing Texan families, Houston decided to retreat, advising all settlers to follow, and ordered the town of Gonzales burned to prevent the Mexicans from gathering anything useful for their campaign.

General Houston, his army, and many settlers retreated east, heading for the Colorado River. The spring of 1836 was wet, and many roads were washed away. The rain, cold, and lack of food and shelter made the settlers susceptible to many diseases, such as cholera, whooping cough, and dysentery. They were buried where they died.

With the Colorado River flooded, the refugees were forced to make crude rafts to cross the swollen waterway. They sank the rafts afterward to delay their Mexican pursuers.

Houston and his followers stayed ahead of the Mexican army by crossing another river, the Brazos. The initial plan was to head toward the United States border, where a federal army under General Edmund Pendleton Gaines had assembled to protect Louisiana if Santa Anna decided to invade the United States.

However, Houston made a bold decision. On April 16, 1836, General Houston's army ended the retreat by turning southwest to march toward the eminent confrontation with the mighty Santa Anna and his army.

Houston established his camp on a grassy field in a place called San Jacinto. Santa Anna did not know Houston's exact position, but he believed he had

Houston cornered on less than three square miles of ground, surrounded by the San Jacinto River, the flooded Buffalo Bayou and the marshes and bay on the east and southeast.

Santa Anna was so confident of a victory over Houston that he made several crucial mistakes. He had divided his army for different assignments. Even so, his total strength for this battle was two battalions—about 1,400 men. On the morning of April 21, Santa Anna decided to rest his army. He settled back to plan the following day's attack. During his army's afternoon siesta, he failed to post sentries or skirmishers around his camp.

At noon, on April 21, Houston held a council of war. The majority of his officers favored waiting for Santa Anna's eventual assault. Houston, however, decided to make his own surprise attack that afternoon.

Houston formed his men into battle lines. They were screened from Mexican view by trees and by a slight ridge that ran across the open prairie between the opposing armies.

The Texas army was ready to meet the enemy.

CHAPTER FIFTEEN

Fighting for Texas

With revolution erupting, what was going to happen to the Indians? Both the Mexicans and the American settlers wanted the Cherokee to side with them. This was dangerous for the Cherokee. If they sided with the loser, the winner would punish them afterward and chase them off their land. They would try to stay neutral.

A lone rider rapidly approached the Cherokee village at Caney Creek. War Eagle raced to slow him down before he reached Chief Bowles's cabin.

"Message from General Houston," the rider called out. The chief appeared in his doorway as the rider jumped from his horse.

"Well, speak up boy. What is it?" War Eagle shouted, as the young rider was hesitant to speak in front of the Cherokee chief.

"War Eagle, get some water for this messenger," the chief scolded. Then he raised his hand to calm the messenger down.

War Eagle stepped back, but he was not about to go for water until he heard the message: "Mexico has captured the Alamo. I am in retreat to the Brazos River. Join me if you will."

After quickly giving the messenger a drink of water, War Eagle turned to his uncle. "What will we do? General Houston is losing the war."

"Brave men can lose the battle. Wise men will win the war."

Having made this statement, Chief Bowles walked into his cabin and closed the door behind him.

Evening shadows filtered the sunlight as the Cherokee villagers somberly went about their chores. What will become of us? Everyone wondered.

Not until the next morning did Chief Bowles call a council. Elders formed the circle around a pit of fire. Women, children, and young braves stood back. The chief, who was eighty years old, listened as several spoke.

For a short time, they had known what it was like to feel freedom. Sam Houston had made them a promise for this homeland. They trusted him and had faith that he would not let them down. How could they not send him warriors to fight the battles?

Anxiously waiting, War Eagle stood by. Chief Bowles would make the final decision. He called before him several young braves and his nephew, War Eagle.

"I am too old to lead the way. You will follow the messenger to join General Houston. The messenger will give him my words: my friend, I give you my best."

War Eagle rode five days to reach the Brazos River.

***

The Battle of San Jacinto

General Sam Houston's followers once again asked, "Will we fight here?"

He replied, "We will fight if we must, but be assured we will accept Santa Anna's surrender before this day is done."

War Eagle, several Cherokee braves, and the messenger had arrived just in time. They quickly found General Houston and gave him Chief Bowles's message. With a warm welcome, Houston acknowledged the Cherokees.

"Thank you for coming, my friends. On this day you are members of the Texas army."

"You have kept your promise to give us our homeland," War Eagle said. "Today we fight for Texas, and we promise to win this battle for you, for Texas."

The Texas militia moving quickly and silently across the high- grass plain, and then when they were only a few dozen yards away, they attacked the Mexicans in broad daylight. It was a complete surprise.

The Mexicans were ill prepared and unarmed. Most were asleep; some were out gathering wood, and the cavalrymen were fetching water on horseback.

Charging Santa Anna's camp, the Texans fired and dropped to the ground, expecting a volley from the Mexicans. This did not happen because the Mexican army consisted primarily of professional soldiers trained to fight in ranks, exchanging volleys with their opponent. Not knowing how to fight these Texas scrappers, Santa Anna's defensive line quickly collapsed, and his troops panicked and fled.

Hundreds of the demoralized and confused Mexican soldiers were driven into the marshes along the river near a bridge. They were shot as they struggled in the water.

General Houston tried to restrain his men, but they ignored him. "The Mexicans are running! Don't stop! Give 'em hell!" they shouted. "Remember the Alamo! Remember Goliad!"

Another cry was loud and clear. It was the battle cry of a Cherokee warrior. War Eagle was proving his strength.

Amid thundering horses' hooves, the clashing of steel blades, and bursts of rifle and cannon fire, War Eagle rushed forward with the Texas infantry when General Houston gave the command.

With a blood-curdling cry, War Eagle threw his hatchet, striking a Mexican soldier and killing him instantly.

Freed from the Mexican soldier's grasp, a young man rolled away, waiting to feel the wrath of War Eagle upon him. Instead, a strong hand reached out and pulled him to his feet. War Eagle and Little Bear came face to face. There he was, the youth who seldom left the sight of his mentor, Sam Houston; the youth whom War Eagle had wondered if he would ever see again. It took a brief moment for them to realize they were both Cherokee. Then, together, they got to work.

General Houston personally led the infantry, posting the Second Volunteer Regiment of Colonel Sidney Sherman together with Juan Seguin's men on his far left, with Colonel Edward Burleson's First Volunteer Regiment next in line. In the center, two small, smoothbore artillery pieces, known as the "Twin Sisters," were wheeled forward under the command of Major George W. Hockley. They were supported by four companies of infantry under Captain Henry Wax Karnes. Colonel Henry Millard's regiment of Texas regulars made up the right wing. To the far right, sixty-one Texas Cavalry men under newly promoted Colonel Mirabeau B. Lamar planned to circle into the Mexicans' left flank.

From the moment of the first charge, the battle was a slaughter. The combat itself lasted just eighteen minutes, but the killing continued for several hours. Seven hundred Mexican soldiers died, 208 were wounded, and 730 were taken prisoner. The Texan militia lost nine men. Thirty were wounded.

One of the wounded was General Sam Houston. During the short but furious fighting, he was shot in the left ankle. His horse was shot from under him. Houston lay wounded, but at the end of the battle, the once proud army of Santa Anna had disintegrated into chaos.

Santa Anna disappeared. He shed his ornate uniform to elude discovery and joined the prisoners. However, when one of the Mexicans saluted him as "el presidente," he was under suspicion.

Unfortunately for Santa Anna, it was well known that he wore silk underwear. So when it was discovered that this same person who had been saluted was also wearing silk underwear, the Texans knew they had captured Santa Anna.

Close by, War Eagle and Little Bear watched as several Texas soldiers placed General Houston under a large tree, making sure he was as comfortable as possible. One thing was clear; the general was not going to leave the battlefield before he confronted Santa Anna.

As the Mexican general stood before him in defeat, Houston decided to spare Santa Anna's life, preferring to negotiate an end to the overall hostilities and the withdrawal from Texas of Santa Anna's remaining army.

There were treaties, one public, and one private. In public, Santa Anna signed the May 14, 1836, Treaty of Velasco. Privately, Santa Anna pledged to try to persuade Mexico to acknowledge Texas's independence in return for an escort back to Mexico. The safe passage never materialized, and Santa Anna was held for six months as prisoner of war.

He was taken to Washington, DC. There, he met with President Andrew Jackson before finally returning to Mexico in disgrace in early 1837. Disowned by his government, Santa Anna would have no influence on an agreement with Mexico for Texan independence.

However, with the defeat of Santa Anna, Texan independence was a fait accompli, although Mexico did not officially recognize it until the Treaty of Guadalupe Hidalgo ended the Mexican–American War in 1848.

Measured by its results, San Jacinto was a decisive battle. Texans won their freedom, which led to a victory in the Mexican-American War, resulting in the acquisition of Texas by the United States.

Texas, New Mexico, Arizona, Nevada, California, Utah, and parts of Colorado, Wyoming, Kansas, and Oklahoma were added to the United States. Almost one-third of the present area of the American nation, nearly a million square miles of territory, changed sovereignty. The United States of America from "coast to coast" was no longer just a vision.

CHAPTER SIXTEEN

Newfound Friend

The mist of twilight hung low over the battlefield. Standing by their fallen hero, General Sam Houston, were two young Cherokee warriors. They had proven their worth on the battlefield, fighting for victory, for Texas, and for their friend, Sam Houston.

Greeting the two Cherokee with a warm smile, the general joked, "Doc says he can chop my foot off or I can go to somewhere in the United States for treatment on my ankle. Which one do you recommend I do?"

Neither answered directly, but their responses were simultaneous: "Shall we go with you?"

"Guess that answers my question. Now the answer to your question is no." The general was adamant. "War Eagle, Little Bear, you two have served me well. Now you must return to the Cherokee. Your people need you. Little Bear, get pen and paper to write this down."

To whom it may concern:

Little Bear is trustworthy, a good writer, good with numbers and a loyal friend. War Eagle is strong in body and a good protector. I recommend anyone give them a job.

Sincerely,

General Sam Houston

As War Eagle and Little Bear said their good-byes to the general and then turned to walk away, the general's last words to them were, "You have a long journey. Territory of Oklahoma, Cherokee Nation of Oklahoma, is the land of your future."

War Eagle asked Little Bear, "Do you trust the words of Sam Houston?"

Little Bear replied, "I trust him with my life."

"Then I guess, my newfound friend, we are on our way to Oklahoma. Have you ever been there?" War Eagle asked.

"I've been there. Don't much like the idea of going back," Little Bear said, sounding doubtful.

"Before I go anywhere," said War Eagle, "I am going to Caney Creek. My uncle waits for me there."

"Your uncle? Who is your uncle?" Little Bear asked. "Chief Bowles is my uncle," War Eagle was proud to say.

"Uncle Bowles will welcome us. I have spent many a night by the fire in his lodge. He is the one that told me to go help his friend, Sam Houston. He said I was always looking for a fight, and Houston had a good one going. It will be great to tell Uncle that we won the fight."

The pair had five days of travel to Caney Creek ahead of them—plenty of time to ask each other about their Cherokee heritage.

War Eagle began with his questions. "Tell me, Little Bear, were you born in this place called Oklahoma? How did you get to know Sam Houston? And how did you get to be called Little Bear?" War Eagle was teasing him now.

"Slow down with all the questions," Little Bear quickly responded.

"First of all, my name is not funny. When I was a little boy, my parents found me playing with a big black bear. Then one day, they found me sound asleep beside the bear. The bear was not moving when they picked me up. It is told that on that day, the spirit of the bear passed to me. All believed that I was indeed 'Little Bear.'"

Stopping his horse, War Eagle sat staring at his new friend. "I, too, believe you have the spirit of the bear, just as I have the spirit of the eagle. My mother named me Little Eagle; Uncle Bowles changed it to War Eagle because as I grew older, I liked to fight."

The two Cherokee laughed as they rode on down the road. Later in the day, as they rested their horses, Little Bear continued to talk about himself. "Twenty-three years ago, I was born in the homeland of all the Cherokee. Land of mountains covered with green trees in the summer and golden leaves of fall; creeks of pure water and rivers with fish; flat land for our gardens and crops. This was our home on the other side of the mighty river. As a boy, I ran and played freely, went to school, and spent many days with my girlfriend.

"At age seventeen, my happy life ended. My parents were told the white man's government was taking our land and moving all the Indians west across the Mississippi River.

"My father, fearing for our safety, loaded the wagon with all we could carry and joined others heading west.

"Some refused to go west, believing they would not be forced to do so. Unfortunately, one of those people refusing to leave was my girlfriend," he said. "I left her behind."

Little Bear reached into his pocket and pulled out a red ribbon. "See this ribbon?" he asked, showing it to War Eagle. "The morning I left, I went to her cabin. I could not bear saying good-bye. I had a red ribbon that belonged to her. I took the ribbon and cut it in half. I tied one half to the latch on her cabin door, and I folded the other half and put it in my pocket."

Amazed at the story, War Eagle said, "And you still have your half."

"Yes," Little Bear said softly. "I will have it until I can put the ribbon back together or until I die."

"Wow, my friend," said War Eagle. "You must really love this girl."

"Yes," replied Little Bear. "Polly is the love of my life."

Conversation was over for the day. Little Bear said that he would tell how he met Sam Houston another time.

War Eagle was not going to let Little Bear stop telling his story. How did he get from crossing the Mississippi to meeting Sam Houston?

"You have heard of miracles," Little Bear began. "It was a true miracle that I survived the day a fierce storm roared down the river toward the boat carrying my family and all our belongings. When it hit, everything was tossed to-and-fro like leaves in the wind. I remember going down, down into the dark water. The next thing I can recall was opening my eyes, looking into the face of a white man. He told me I was now on the deck of a boat, far away from where I had been pulled out of the water.

"I was saved. My family was not," Little Bear said.

"The white man was kind and saw that I had passage on the boat to Oklahoma. Many Indians were on the same boat. When the boat landed and everyone got off, I do not know what happened to the others. I walked to a nearby fort. The soldiers of the fort paid little attention to me. I was just a homeless Indian getting food and a place to sleep where I could find it.

"The soldiers amused themselves by giving me liquor and teasing me when I got drunk. Lying in the gutter, I shivered. I was cold and wet, near death. Two large hands reached down and picked me up. I had never seen such a big white man.

"He took me to the back of the general store, where I washed myself. A set of new, clean clothes was brought to me. A large plate of food was brought to me. For some time, I sat by the potbelly stove. The large man came and spoke to me. He said he was called Colon-neh (the Raven).

"Waiting outside the store were several men on horseback and one horse for me. I was not afraid of the horse. He stood still as I settled into the saddle. I followed the big man out of the fort.

"Feeling the cool air on my face, seeing and hearing the sights and sounds of nature, I was free. My Little Bear spirit awakened.

Pride filled my soul. I rode with Sam Houston on the road to Texas."

Exaggerating where possible, War Eagle told Little Bear about himself. There was no way his life story could be as dramatic as Little Bear's, but by the end of the road trip, each was proud of his newfound friend.

Arriving at the Cherokee encampment on Caney Creek, the young men were welcomed by Chief Bowles.

"So, you have returned victorious, War Eagle. I hear good fighting for Texas and my friend, Sam Houston," said the Cherokee chief.

"Yes, Uncle," replied War Eagle. "General Houston won the battle, but he is wounded."

Chief Bowles looked at Little Bear. "Why do you leave our friend when he is wounded?"

Quickly, War Eagle explained, "It was General Houston who sent us away. He is going to the States for treatment of his wounded ankle. He has given us a paper and told us to go to Oklahoma."

After the two warriors had eaten a meal, Chief Bowles invited them to sit with him in his lodge while he smoked his pipe.

The two knew that this meant a serious discussion was going to take place.

"It is good you have returned to our people," the chief began. "I fear we all may go to Oklahoma. With Sam Houston leaving Texas, we do not trust the white Texans. They will break their promise to leave us be.

"In my dreams, the wind blows strong, destroys our lodges, takes our women and children. We fight our battle. We will not win. Our people will all go to Oklahoma; I will not."

Little Bear did not know what to think of the chief's ramblings, but War Eagle seemed to understand his meaning. When they left the chief, he said to Little Bear, "I think we should stay with Uncle for a while in case his dreams speak the truth."

Little Bear agreed.

CHAPTER SEVENTEEN

Texas is Free but the

Cherokee are Not

With the battle for freedom fought and won, the Anglo- Texans declared their independence from Mexico with a sense of security. The first congress of the Republic of Texas convened in October 1836.

After returning to Texas from the United States, his battle wound healed, Sam Houston became the first president of the Republic of Texas.

Another Texas hero, Stephen F. Austin, returned to Texas from prison in Mexico to become the secretary of state for the new republic. Serving only two months as secretary, Austin, known as the Father of Texas, died on December 27, 1836.

Shortly after the government of the Republic of Texas was set up, the Texas Cherokee became concerned about the title to their land. Sam Houston tried to get the 1836 treaty ratified by the new Texas government. It did nothing about the treaty until 1837, when the Texas Senate rejected the treaty signed by Houston and several others and agreed to by Cherokee Chief Bowles. Although the Republic of Texas legislators declared the treaty null and void, Sam Houston always maintained that the treaty was binding.

Still, while Houston was president, things were all right for the Texas Cherokee. Then Texas elected a new president, Mirabeau Lamar. Lamar did not like the Cherokees—or any Indians, for that matter—and he said so. Lamar and others were convinced that the Mexicans were trying to get the Cherokee to help them take back Texas.

The truth was that Lamar wanted the Cherokee out of Texas so American settlers could take their land. He made this clear in a letter to Cherokee Chief Bowles, written on May 26, 1839.

Here is part of the letter that President Mirabeau Bonaparte Lamar sent to Cherokee Chief Bowles, also named Chief Duwa'li:

I therefore feel it to be my duty as Chief Magistrate of this republic, to tell you, in the plain language of sincerity, that the Cherokee will never be permitted to establish a permanent and independent jurisdiction within the inhabited limits of this government; that the political and fee-simple claims, which they set up to our territory now occupied by them, will never be allowed, and that they are permitted, at present, to remain where they are only because this government is looking forward to the time, when some peaceable arrangements can be made for their removal, without the shedding of blood, but that their final removal is contemplated, is certain: and that it will be affected, is equally so. Whether it be done by friendly negotiation or by violence of war, must depend on the Cherokee themselves...

President Lamar ordered soldiers to keep an eye on the Cherokee. Intercepting a Mexican emissary, the soldiers found a letter to Chief Bowles. The letter's contents were interpreted to mean that the Cherokee were in league with Mexican officials. Sam Houston was never convinced that this was true.

Responding to this letter, President Lamar sent an Indian agent, Martin Lacy, to confer with Chief Bowles.

Arriving at the Cherokee village, Lacy, John A. Reagan, Dr. W. G. W. Jowers, and an interpreter named Cordra were received politely. They were seated on a log near a creek, a short distance from Chief Bowles's cabin.

Lacy did not hesitate to accuse the Cherokee of cooperating with Mexico to continue its fight against Texas. He also accused the Cherokee of stealing and committing certain murders.

The Cherokee chief denied the allegations and stated that he could not respond to the Texas government's request that the Cherokee leave Texas until he had council with the tribe.

Outraged by the report of Lacy's meeting with Chief Bowles, President Lamar ordered the old chief to be sent a message: your people will be moved beyond the Red River "peaceably if they would; forcibly if they must."

The chief was granted ten days to give his answer.

When he returned for Chief Bowles's reply, Agent Lacy found the old chief very grave. His entire council had agreed to fight the Anglo-Texans for rights to the land.

The eighty-three-year-old chief said that in the course of nature, he probably had few years to live, and he was concerned about his family and the survival of the Texas Cherokee.

"If I fight, the whites will kill me. If I refuse to fight, my own people will kill me," Chief Bowles said. "I have led my people for a long time, and I feel that it is my duty to stand by them regardless of what fate might befall me."

The Last Battle between the Texas Cavalry and the Cherokee

In July 1839, President Lamar sent troops to remove the Cherokee from their home. Chief Bowles tried to lead his people north along the Neches River to escape, but the Texas militia pursued them. On July 15, 1839, Chief Bowles led his braves into battle.

According to eyewitness accounts, Chief Bowles, eighty-three years old, stayed at the front of his men during the entire battle.

The fighting was cruel, and there were many casualties.

Realizing the battle was lost, the old chief found his nephew, War Eagle, who was fighting alongside his friend, Little Bear.

"War Eagle, you and Little Bear go!" Chief Bowles yelled over the battle noise. "Ride to the Red River. Cross the river. You must live."

War Eagle was not going to leave his uncle.

The old chief raised his spear and shouted, "Leave! Now!" Obeying his uncle, War Eagle called out to Little Bear,

"Let's ride!"

Other Cherokee on the battlefield, seeing War Eagle riding away and knowing the battle was lost, retreated. Chief Bowles stayed on the battlefield with the last of his men to help all who could retreat do so safely.

Chief Bowles was shot in the leg, and his horse was wounded.

The chief climbed down from his horse and started to walk from the battlefield. He was shot in the back.

The eighty-three-year-old chief sat down, crossing his arms and legs, and faced the Texas militia. As he sat dying, a militiaman came up, placed a pistol to his head, and killed him. It has been said that militia members took strips of skin from the chief 's arms as souvenirs. His body was left where it lay. No burial ever took place. No funeral service was held for Cherokee Chief Duwa'li Bowles until some 156 years after his death.

The Texas Cavalry won the last battle with the Cherokee in Texas. Chief Bowles was dead along with over one hundred other Cherokee.

The remaining Cherokee were driven across the Red River into Indian Territory. Some Cherokee continued to live a fugitive existence in Texas, while others took up residence in Mexico. A few even continued the fight against the Texans but with little success.

As Ira Kennedy, a descendant of the Texas Cherokee, said in *A Brief History of the Texas*

Cherokee, "A few men with ambitious dreams had demolished one nation, the Texas Cherokee, and at the same time, paved the way for another, the Republic of Texas."

Historical Facts

Presidents of the United States from 1809 to 1841

- **James Madison**: b. 3/16/1751, d. 6/28/1836, term of office: 1809–1817; Fourth president of the United States. Helped draft the US Constitution. He proposed the first ten amendments to the Constitution, the Bill of Rights. President during the War of 1812 against England. Married to Dolley Payne Todd, who is said to have rescued a portrait of George Washington when the British burned Washington, DC, in 1814.

- **James Monroe**: b. 4/28/1758, d. 7/4/1831, term of office: 1817–1825; Fifth president of the United States. His most important accomplishment was the Monroe Doctrine, an important statement of US foreign policy. It warned European countries not to try to set up new colonies in the Americas and not to interfere in the affairs of the countries in the Americas. From the very beginning of his presidency, there was a new feeling of national unity. It was a period of peace and prosperity known as the "era of good feeling." His wife, Elizabeth Kortright, became the first First Lady of the present

White House in 1817.

- **John Quincy Adams**: b. 7/11/1767, d. 2/23/1848, term of office: 1825–1829; Sixth president of the United States. He was the son of John Adams, the second president. He negotiated the treaty that ended the War of 1812 with Britain, negotiated the treaty with Britain that placed the portion of the US- Canadian border that lies west of the Great Lakes along the forty-ninth parallel, and negotiated a treaty with Spain that gave Florida to the United States. Many roads and canals were built during this period, and the country prospered. From 1831 until his death in 1848, he served in the House of Representatives. There, he fought for the protection of Indian tribes.

- **Andrew Jackson**: b. 3/15/1767, d. 6/8/1845, term of office: 1829–1837; Seventh president of the United States. He was the first president to rise from humble origins. He became a national hero after he served as a major general in the War of 1812, defeating the Creek Indians and routing the British in the Battle of New Orleans. He was in favor of state's rights. As president, he supported the Southern states that forcibly expelled their Indian populations in spite of federal treaties and court decisions.

- **Martin Van Buren**: b. 12/5/1782, d. 7/24/1862, term of office: 1837–1841; Eighth president of the United States. He served in a time when the United States was suffering a great economic depression. The financial collapse occurred in the first year of his presidency. Soup kitchens were the only source of food for many people who lost their savings in the panic of 1837. Thousands of people were put out of work, and they hoped that the government would help. But Van Buren believed that the government should not interfere in the economy. He believed that private business could best end the depression. The depression spoiled his reputation as a friend of labor and the working person. He lost the next election.

***

The Cherokees' Introduction to Texas

- **Land**: The idea of "owning" land was foreign to the American Indian, who could not conceive of owning the earth—until the land was taken away. The Indians believed that they were stewards of the earth, but the white man had a different understanding of land. When the Cherokee moved into Texas, they became the dominant Indian tribe in East Texas. They made treaties with the Anglo-Americans in order to call this area their homeland. White settlers created an uncontrolled momentum to break any promise by the American government because of their desire for Indian lands. The Cherokee's good fortune of finding a new homeland was, indeed, too good to be true.

- **Caney Creek**: Site of the Cherokee settlement founded by the Cherokee leader, Bowles. Caney Creek is located about fifty miles north of Nacogdoches, Texas. In 1819, Chief Bowles was anxious to escape the jurisdiction of the United States where the Cherokee were settled on the Arkansas River. He took sixty families with him, and they moved to Caney Creek. In 1838, the Texas Cherokee were forced to leave their settlement.

- **Nacogdoches:** Known as the oldest town in Texas, located approximately 140 miles north-northeast of Houston, 180 miles southeast of Dallas, and 90 miles southwest of Shreveport, Louisiana. Evidence of settlement on the same site dates back 10,000 years. It is near or on the site of Nevantin, the primary village of the Nacogdoches tribe of Caddo Indians. Nacogdoches remained a Caddo Indian settlement until early nineteenth century. In 1716, the Spanish established a mission there. People from the United States began to settle in Nacogdoches in 1820. Sam Houston lived in Nacogdoches for four years, from 1832 to 1836.

Wars to Free Mexico

- **The Alamo**: The Battle of the Alamo, February 23 to March 6, 1836, has captured the imagination of people around the world. The Alamo was a mission turned into a fort at San Antonio, Texas. The battle was conspicuous for the large number of illustrious personalities among the combatants. These included Tennessee Congressman Davy Crockett, entrepreneur and adventurer James Bowie, and Mexican President Antonio Lopez de Santa Anna. William Barret Travis was the Texans' commander of the Alamo. Mexico won the battle, but for many Americans and most Texans, the battle has become a symbol of patriotic sacrifice. Traditional popular depictions, including novels, stage plays, and motion pictures, emphasize this legendary aspect. Americans on battlefields around the globe have responded to the exhortation, "Remember the Alamo!"

- **Goliad**: On March 27, 1836, General Santa Anna of Mexico ordered the execution of some 380 Texas army soldiers who were prisoners of war. The men were part of the command of Colonel James W. Fannin Jr., and they had surrendered to the Mexican army on March 20, 1836, at the battle of Coleto Creek. Fannin had received assurances from the Mexican field commander, General Jose de Urrea, that the Texans would eventually be paroled and sent to New Orleans. Although Urrea probably had good intentions, Santa Anna overruled him and commanded that the prisoners be slaughtered.

- **Goliad, the Massacre**: The execution of Fannin's soldiers at Goliad branded Santa Anna as an inhuman despot and the Mexican people, whether deserved or not, with a reputation for cruelty. Because of the needless slaughter, a burning desire for revenge arose among the people of Texas, and Americans became firmly united behind the Texas cause of independence.

- **Battle of San Jacinto**: Fought on April 21, 1836, near La Porte, Texas, in present-day Harris County, Texas. The Texan army led by General Sam Houston engaged and defeated General Antonio Lopez de Santa Anna's Mexican forces. This was the decisive battle of the

Texas Revolution. The Mexican president, Santa Anna, was captured, and Sam Houston became a national celebrity.

- **Battle of the Neches**: On July 15 and 16, 1839, the last battle was fought between the Texas Cavalry and Cherokee in Texas. In July 1839, Texas sent troops to remove the Cherokee from their homes in Texas. Cherokee Chief Bowles tried to lead his people north along the Neches River to escape, but the Texas militia pursued them. A fierce battle took place near the headwaters of the Neches River in what is now Van Zandt County, Texas. The Cherokee chief was killed along with over one hundred other Cherokees. The Texas Cherokee moved to Indian Territory in what is now Oklahoma. In 1936, the state of Texas erected a marker on the site where the last engagement between the Cherokee and whites in Texas took place. On November 25, 1997, the American Indian Heritage Center of Texas Inc., a Texas nonprofit organization, purchased the land where the Battle of Neches was fought in Van Zandt County, Texas, near the community of Redland.

***

Men Who Shaped Texas

- **General Antonio Lopez de Santa Anna**: In 1824, Santa Anna declared himself supreme dictator of Mexico. By 1835, he had defeated all militia against him in Mexico. He marched his army north into Texas. There, he succeeded in defeating and massacring the Texas garrison at the Alamo on March 6, 1836, and at Goliad three weeks later. On April 21, 1836, Santa Anna was defeated by the Republic of Texas army led by Sam Houston at the Battle of San Jacinto. Santa Anna's failure to post lookouts properly proved fatal. At 3:30 p.m., the general was taking a nap when Houston attacked.

- **Sam Houston in Texas**: 1832–1836: He practiced law and lived in Nacogdoches, Texas. 1835: Commissioned major general in the Texas Army. 1836: On March 2, signed the Texas Declaration of Independence. 1836: On April 21, defeated Antonio Lopez de Santa Anna, the Mexican president, at the Battle of San Jacinto. 1836: On September 5, elected president of Republic of Texas. He served from October 22, 1836, to December 10, 1838, and again from December 12, 1841, to December 1844.

- **Stephen F. Austin**: Known as the Father of Texas. He believed in government authority. After trying to work with the Mexican government, he committed himself to the cause of an independent Texas. When the first congress of the Republic of Texas convened in October 1836, Austin was appointed secretary of state for the new republic. After serving for just two months, he died on December 27, 1836. The capital city of Texas is named in his honor.

- **Cherokee Chief Bowles (Duwa' li)**: 1819: He moved his tribe into Texas, settling north of Nacogdoches. 1822: He sent his diplomatic chief to Mexico to negotiate with the Spanish government for a land grant or title to the land occupied by Cherokee in East Texas. 1833: He made another attempt to secure the land from the Mexican government, but negotiations were interrupted by political unrest in Texas. 1836: Sam Houston negotiated a treaty with Chief Bowles and council, guaranteeing the tribe ownership of the land it occupied in East Texas. 1838: After the Texas Revolution and once Sam Houston was replaced by Mirabeau B. Lamar as president, the Senate of the Republic of Texas invalidated the treaty. Lamar ordered the Cherokee to leave Texas. Chief Bowles mobilized his warriors to resist expulsion. The paramount motive for all of his actions was to secure a single piece of paper that would grant his people legal rights to their settlement in Texas. 1839: On July 16, Chief Bowles died in the Battle of Neches. No burial ever took place. No funeral service was held until some 156 years after his death. On Sunday, July 16, 1995, descendants of the Texas Cherokee tribe and their friends met to honor Chief Bowles with a funeral service and to remember the others whose lives were lost in the battle. This funeral was held on the site of the Battle of Neches in Van Zandt County, Texas.

Part Three

CHAPTER EIGHTEEN

Leaving the Red River Valley

Fleeing the sting of battle and the agony of defeat, the retreating Texas Cherokee reached the north side of the Red River.

Most had never known life without the Red River waters or walked a land other than its valley. Their cries pierced the summer air as they called upon the Great Spirit. Lingering at river's edge, many washed their bloodstained clothes; others pressed on with all their strength. They prayed for help in their unknown land.

***

War Eagle

A creature of nature, filled with the creator's spirit, War Eagle, Texas Cherokee, stood tall on a boulder at the water's edge. His strong body was clothed as a Cherokee warrior; his long hair caught the breeze and brushed his shoulders.

Reaching for the sky, he heard a cry in the wind. He waited.

With the setting of the evening sun, the eagle appeared.

His majestic wings in flight, for only a moment did his talons touch the outstretched hands. The eyes of the eagle looked upon the face of a man, no longer that little boy playing down by the river.

A farewell was shared as one called to the other. One would keep guard over the waters of the Red River; one would leave for parts unknown. All that mattered was that two spirits were as one.

Never forgotten, the eagle spirit lived in the soul of the one called War Eagle, Texas Cherokee.

***

Texas Cherokee

Left to rot on the battlefield, the bones of the eighty-three- year-old Chief Bowles lay on display for years afterward. The Indians were defeated; another battle had been lost.

Suffering humiliation so many times, the Cherokee Indians remained strong in their beliefs and bonds with nature and each other. Seeking a new homeland for their people, leaders of the tribes had found a place called Texas. West of the great Mississippi River, where they dared to hope for prosperity and dreamed of freedom, the Cherokee built homes with farms on banks of rivers in east Texas. The value of their property grew because of their hunting and farming skills. They were frontiers people, but they always maintained their identity as Native Americans.

Perhaps this identity is what made the Anglo-Americans think they could migrate by the thousands into Texas and occupy all the land.

The year 1839 found the Texas Cherokee fighting for their land. They were no match for the Texas military. More than one hundred Indians, including Chief Bowles, were killed in that final conflict. The remaining Cherokee were driven across the Red River into what had become the white man's Indian Territory. Some Cherokee did continue to live a fugitive existence in Texas, while others took up residence in Mexico. A few even continued the fight against the Texans but with no success.

The Texas Cherokee were forced north of the Red River into Indian Territory in what is now Oklahoma. There, they were reunited with some 6,000 Eastern Cherokee. In the beginning, they had all lived east of the Mississippi River; now they all had been forced to move from their homelands.

The final solution to remove Eastern Cherokee to west of the Mississippi River came when the government of the United States forced them to move off their land.

Cherokee men, women, children and babies, the elderly, and the sick were all marched at gunpoint by army troops to the Indian Territory in Oklahoma during the winter of 1838–1839.

Many of them died along the way from the cold and from starvation because the army would not feed them properly.

This forced march of the Eastern Cherokee is remembered as The Trail of Tears because so many suffered and so many died.

When the Texas Cherokee, forced north of the Red River, arrived in the northeastern corner of the Indian Territory of Oklahoma, they were the destitute newcomers and, naturally, caused problems for the Eastern Cherokee who had already settled in that area.

The white-American government had succeeded in moving the Cherokee off their homelands and at the same time splintered the Cherokee nation.

Early 1840, a man they called "Walk-A-Bout" journeyed through northeast Texas in an attempt to reunite the scattered members of the Cherokee tribe.

His walk west had two purposes: to unite the Cherokee nation and to create a syllabary for use among all Native American tribes.

Being in declining health due to advancing age, Walk-A- Bout grew ill on the trek and shortly thereafter passed away. A gravesite near a freshwater spring in Coahuila, Mexico, may be his, although many believe that he passed away on what is now Red River tribal land.

Jack Kilpatrick wrote, "Sequoyah was always in the wilderness. He walked about, but he was not a hunter. I wonder what he was looking for."

The Texas Cherokee, the Eastern Cherokee, and all others were united in their pride for the beloved Sequoyah. Perhaps now he has joined War Eagle's father, Sky Walker, and they walk together on the other side of the sky.

CHAPTER NINETEEN

Road to Tahlequah

Sky as far as the eye can see—a vast space as it touched the earth in the distant vision.

Sun and moon, rain and rainbows, War Eagle began his journey to find his sense of place. As he rode into Oklahoma Territory, riding with him were the spirits of his ancestors. Connecting with the memories of all that had gone before, he found his energy from spirits of the eagle, Red River Valley, and the Texas Cherokee.

In all that was and all that would be; in every sound, every touch, taste, and smell; he listened to hear water speaking, wind dancing, to see the sun smiling, and feel the heartbeat of the earth pulsing beneath his feet.

War Eagle entered a new world for him. With strength of body and mind, he was armed with humility, kindness, wonder, and respect for all living things. On his journey forward, he would leave a trail for those yet to come—a trail of harmony and balance.

Twice passed the sun and the moon before War Eagle caught up with his friend, Little Bear.

"Hey, little bother," War Eagle called out, "wait for me. You didn't think you were gonna leave me behind, did you?"

"I knew you would find me sooner or later." Little Bear laughed a little.

Finding shade from the summer sun, the two were joined by a few other Cherokee, resting their horses. They tried to make sense out of what had happened to their lives in Texas. There seem to be no reason for the loss of their homes and many of their people. But once again, they must search for a home, a place for another new beginning.

Following Little Bear, War Eagle and his small band of Texas Cherokee reached Fort Smith, Oklahoma.

Having no fond memories of his earlier time at Fort Smith, Little Bear was eager to get on the road again.

"OK, Little Bear, I followed you. Now you follow me," War Eagle said with confidence.

North by northwest, they followed directions to Fort Gibson. Leaving the others behind, they were able to travel faster, and once they reached Fort Gibson, they had no trouble in locating the trading post, Wigwam Neosho. Walking into the front room of the trading post, the two Cherokee did as Sam Houston had told them.

"I would like to speak to a lady named Tiana," Little Bear said to an elderly man who was seated near the front door.

Looking the two young men over, the man answered, "And who would you be?"

War Eagle and Little Bear looked at each other, sensing hostility from the old man. Surely, he would change his attitude when they told him they had been sent by Mr. Sam Houston. He didn't.

"Well, well sent by Sam Houston, are you? He is a little late to be sending for his wife." The man stood up in a defensive manner.

War Eagle and Little Bear quickly assured the man that they were not there to pick up anyone. Showing him the paper from Sam Houston, they stated that their purpose was to get jobs.

The man took the paper, read it, and then handed it back. "I apologize for being short with you boys. The lady you are looking for to receive this paper is dead. She died last week with pneumonia.

"You can tell your Mr. Houston that I have no work for you Cherokee. I am John McGrady. After Mr. Houston rode off to Texas, leaving his Cherokee wife, I married her. Tiana was a good wife, but she never gave up looking for this Sam Houston fellow to come back. So, I run this place now without her," McGrady said. "If the words on that paper are true, ride on up to Tahlequah," "Sure you can get a job there. Tahlequah is now the capital for your people."

As War Eagle turned to leave, he could not resist saying a few last words. "Sorry for your loss, sir. We will go to Tahlequah," he said. "Oh, and don't worry; Mr. Houston won't be coming back to Oklahoma. He is the president of Texas now."

When they got to their horses, War Eagle and Little Bear mocked the man.

"My wife is dead; Mr. Houston is gone. I, John McGrady, own the place. Got that, boys? No jobs for you."

"Forget him," said Little Bear. "If only Cherokee live in Tahlequah, could be a good place for us."

"Let's ride." War Eagle gave his warrior call.

CHAPTER TWENTY

Tahlequah

Wearing his traditional Cherokee clothing—deerskin shirt and pants with a breechcloth—War Eagle felt the pride of his Cherokee people as he rode into Tahlequah.

The clothing of Little Bear had changed years earlier when the coming of the Europeans changed many things.

"With your short haircut and those white man's clothes, you don't look much like an Indian," War Eagle said, laughing. "But I don't hold that against you."

"Don't worry about my clothes," Little Bear snapped. "Clothes don't make a man."

As they soon found out, their clothing didn't matter; everyone they met accepted both men as Cherokee and offered their help.

The old man at the livery stable told them they could leave their horses with him, free of charge, while they looked for work.

Several days passed; showing everyone they met the letter from Sam Houston wasn't helping the two find work. All knew of Sam Houston; they just did not have jobs for his friends.

All hope of finding work in Tahlequah faded. War Eagle and Little Bear agreed they should leave that place, search for a place where they could live off the land. Hunt and fish, they could live as their ancestors had survived.

Walking to the livery stable to get their horses, War Eagle assured his friend that he knew how to live the old Cherokee way.

Spotting a young woman carrying some books in her arms and trying to cross mud puddles without dropping them, it was War Eagle to the rescue.

"Here, let me help you," he said as he reached for the books. "Thank you, kind sir." She was grateful for his help as she handed him her books.

"These books are heavy. May I carry them to the schoolhouse for you?" War Eagle was hopeful.

"How do you know I am going to the schoolhouse?" she questioned.

"Where else would books be going?" teased War Eagle. Making her way through the mud puddles, she smiled. "Yes, thank you, if it is not too much trouble."

War Eagle, the flirt, was always swooning over the pretty, young women. Little Bear would just wait for him at the livery stable and listen to the tall tales War Eagle would be telling him for days.

"Come with me, come with me! You are not going to believe it!" War Eagle screamed as he ran toward the livery stable.

"OK, OK," Little Bear said, calming his friend down. "What kinda trouble are we in now?"

"No trouble, my friend. I may have found a job for both of us, and I didn't even need the paper from Mr. Houston. You can thank me."

Upon reaching the schoolhouse, War Eagle searched for the young woman, but a large, robust Indian fellow met them at the door.

"Show him the paper from Mr. Houston," War Eagle said, nervous.

After reading the letter from Sam Houston, the man turned to Little Bear. "Do you read and write the Sequoyah?"

"Yes, sir, I do. Wrote that letter you are holding. I read and write English and Cherokee. Learned in a mission school in my homeland in the East." Little Bear was impressive.

"And you, what is it you do?" the man asked, turning to War Eagle.

"I am a brave warrior. Helped Sam Houston free Texas, and I can guard your school, no problem. There will be no stealing of books while I am here," War Eagle bragged.

"Oh, I am sure of that," said the man, chuckling, as he invited them into his office.

Wasting no time, he offered jobs to both.

"Mr. Little Bear, you can teach the children. And you, Mr. War Eagle, can guard the teacher. Oh yes, and the books."

"You can tell me later if you want the jobs and we will talk of wages," he said. "Look around and if you have any questions, I am Principal John."

War Eagle had but one question. "Where is the young woman that brought me here?"

Principal John turned and walked out of the room. He did not answer the question.

CHAPTER TWENTY-ONE

Tamara

With some advance wages, War Eagle and Little Bear secured their rooms at the boarding house and paid the man at the livery stable the fee for keeping their horses.

Mr. John, the school principal, negotiated credit at the dry goods store for proper clothing for his new employees.

The new job was not the only thing on War Eagle's mind.

Looking upon her one day as she left the schoolhouse, he couldn't take his eyes off her. For days, he watched from afar.

Running from tree to tree, he followed her home.

Feeling the chill of the autumn air, she wrapped her shawl around her shoulders. Two steps from her porch, she stopped and turned toward the thicket nearby. "Had you not rather walk beside me to and from the schoolhouse, or do you wish to go from tree to tree?"

His hide and seek was over. He was caught. Looking back on that day some years later, War Eagle said he was not only caught but also captured for the rest of his life.

Questioning Little Bear, War Eagle asked, "Have you met the beautiful lady school teacher?"

"Only briefly," responded Little Bear. "I have been so busy setting up my new classroom; no time for anything else."

"Come with me today when I walk her home. She has been asking questions about you. Only beware, my friend, she is my girlfriend." War Eagle wanted that to be clear.

"OK, OK; if you insist, I will talk with your friend," Little Bear said. But to himself, he said she was just another one in War Eagle's long list of sweethearts.

In the afternoon, the two friends waited outside the schoolhouse. When she approached, they did not touch her. It was Little Bear who stared into her black eyes and embraced her warm smile.

Tapping him on the shoulder, War Eagle broke the long silence. "You are staring; say hello."

"Well?" he said, growing anxious. "Someone say something."

Slowly placing her hands to her lips, she said in soft, sweet voice, "Little Bear, Little Bear, Little Bear."

Tears filled her eyes. Reaching out to him, she cried, "Little Bear, it is you, my brother, Little Bear."

Holding her back to look upon her face, Little Bear could barely say, "Tamara. Is your name Tamara?"

For the first time in ten years, she replied, "Yes, I am Tamara." "My sister, my sister," were Little Bear's only words as they cried together.

War Eagle, feeling ignored and confused, asked, "What is this? I thought your name was Miracle Child and your brother drowned years ago."

"Poor War Eagle, we do have a lot to explain since you are to be my husband." Tamara was now joyful.

Long hours of storytelling followed brother and sister's discovery of each other. After many suns and many moons apart, from now on all days would be shared together and with a new member of their family, War Eagle.

Tamara stood in front of her classroom as the Cherokee children waited patiently. She told her story:

Many moons ago, I left my homeland on the eastern side of the great river.

The white men put our wagon on a big, flat boat to ride on many waters.

One day on the river, the sunlight turned to black of night. I was alone in the wagon when the wind picked the wagon up and tossed it into the woods.

Out of the river, into the wilderness, the riverbanks prevented anyone from seeing the wagon.

I was asleep, and when I woke up, a strange Indian man stood over me. He was not of the Cherokee. He took me to be with the Osage people. They called me Miracle Child. Over time, my memory faded of my mother, father, and brother.

I was sure they were dead. The only way I could survive that tragic day was to forget. I talked to no one of it, not even telling my name. I grew for years as the Miracle Child. Before the Indian man that found me died, he brought me to Tahlequah so I could become a teacher. I knew some English and some Sequoyah alphabet. I was quick to learn and proud to say the English alphabet backward as fast as I can say it forward.

I spent nine years with the Osage Indians. The kindness of a stranger returned me to my people. Because of the Osage Indian man, I would not be denied my Cherokee heritage.

Now I am so happy. I have found my brother, who also survived that tragic day. He is our teacher, Little Bear. On another day, he will tell his story.

The children clapped as Tamara made her way to the back of the classroom and embraced her brother, Little Bear. Oh yes, she could not leave War Eagle out; she embraced him also.

CHAPTER TWENTY-TWO
Finding Home

War Eagle had stumbled across love without meaning to. His journey had always been filled with fighting, though he was not always sure of what he was fighting for.

Leaving the Red River Valley, his memories of home would never be lost. Life for War Eagle and the Texas Cherokee had changed; their place of home would change.

War Eagle's home with his grandmother and Uncle Bowles had been familiar and comfortable, and they had inspired him to be more than expected, always and forever.

Grandmother taught him the purpose of spirit and the joys of nature.

"Take the time to notice the rainbow that hangs in the sky," was a saying of Grandmother's never to be forgotten.

On the other hand, Uncle Bowles taught him of the harsher things in life. Never take food hot; never drink much water; be observant and a good student of nature; to be a good husband, you must be able to bring home plenty of meat; above all, you must be a good warrior.

War Eagle seemed to take the warrior part very seriously, as he went about fighting much of the time.

Searching for a place to belong, he ran right into a place of connection to his heart that was full of belonging.

His friend, Little Bear, had told him of his love for a girl named Polly. The story of the red ribbon brought tears to War Eagle's eyes.

His wishes and hopes for a true love had been only a silent dream.

Little Bear tapped him on the shoulder. "War Eagle, are you in love with my sister?"

"As true as Mother Earth, the ground upon which we walk, I love Tamara. Do you think she will be my wife?" The warrior was now nervous.

The teacher, Little Bear, responded, "Let your footsteps fall lightly upon the ground; come down upon your knees, press your hands together. After you ask her, listen closely to her answer."

Following those directions, War Eagle waited for her answer.

Softly and quietly, Tamara touched his lips. "I have nothing to give you."

"Your saying yes to my question will give me everything," he said gently.

"Then yes, my answer is yes." Her cheeks were wet with tears of joy.

Most everyone in Tahlequah attended the Cherokee wedding ceremony. War Eagle, the handsome Cherokee warrior, and Tamara, the beautiful young schoolteacher, made a lovely couple.

In the shelter of the trees, the Cherokee community built the newlyweds a cabin. Although the chilly winds of October sometimes rocked the trees, warmed by the sun, the cabin was a place of home.

Happy for his sister and his best friend, Little Bear was sometimes overwhelmed by the loneliness in his heart for his homeland in the East and his love of Polly.

War Eagle had been lucky. His father, Sky Walker, and his Uncle Bowles had brought his Cherokee family west of the Mississippi before the final solution was made by the white man's government.

By the winter of 1838–1839, all Cherokee Indians living east of the Mississippi River were to be forced to move west.

With news of the forced removal, Little Bear was eager to find out if Polly would find her way to him.

"Don't wait for her to find you," War Eagle told Little Bear. "Go search the camps for your sweetheart."

With Tamara filling in for him as a teacher at school and armed with information he received as a council member of the Cherokee capital of Tahlequah, Little Bear was relentless in his search for Polly.

Almost unbearable was the sight of the Cherokee as they reached the camps in Arkansas, Oklahoma, and Missouri.

The route they were forced to travel would forever be called The Trail of Tears.

With War Eagle and Tamara's constant encouragement, Little Bear was hopeful as he looked carefully at every young woman he encountered. He tried to imagine Polly now twenty- five years old. He could only describe her as he knew her over nine years earlier. His one certainty was that if anyone had ever met her, he would remember such a beautiful Cherokee woman.

Just as he was about to give up, Little Bear was told about a group of Cherokee known as the John Benge party, numbering 1,000, that had departed from Fort Payne, Alabama. They left Fort Payne on December 1, 1838, but were delayed at the Mississippi River because it was clogged with ice. After camping for a time, they were ferried across the Mississippi River. Traveling on land through the southeastern corner of Missouri, they arrived in Arkansas in December 1838. The group reached its final destination, Indian Territory, in January 1839.

"This has to be it! She is here," Little Bear said repeatedly to himself. His excitement carried him for days despite the holes in the soles of his shoes, the blisters on his feet, and the lack of sleep. He had little food and almost no energy left. This was his last hope of finding Polly.

Soaking his feet in the river water, remembering how Polly wiggled her toes in the water of the creeks, tears wet his cheeks. He could carry the burden no longer.

Reaching into his pocket, Little Bear pulled out the red ribbon. As it slipped through his fingers, he murmured, "Let her go, let her go."

The ripple of the river
The setting sun
The twilight songs
Another day is done.

He clutched the red ribbon, folded it neatly, and put it back in his pocket. "Not today, Polly; not today."

Lonely and depressed, there was only one place to go. Looking down the trail, he saw his friend War Eagle with two horses.

No words were spoken by Little Bear, only the words from War Eagle. "Come on, brother, let's go home."

CHAPTER

TWENTY-THREE

Time Changes Everything

Many dawns would break as War Eagle and Little Bear discussed their feelings of guilt about helping the white man take the land of Texas while their Cherokee people endured the Trail of Tears.

Pacing the yard, speaking in a loud voice, War Eagle was adamant. "Well, I'm saying I am glad I fought with Sam Houston to save his Texas, and I am glad I fought with Uncle Bowles for our home on Carney Creek.

"One fight, we won; the other, we lost. I wish I had been in the fight to kill the men who betrayed our people in the East."

"War Eagle, you always like a good fight. Bet my sister gives you a good fight now and again," teased Little Bear.

"That she does, my brother, but the only trouble with that is she always wins," complained War Eagle.

"As it should be, my brother, as it should be," Little Bear laughed at the thought of it as he patted War Eagle on the shoulder.

"I can hear you two," Tamara said as she came out the front door.

Just the sight of Tamara filled the air with a sense of joy. The way she tossed her hair as she looked at her brother and the way she pointed her finger at her husband made the two of them laugh aloud. But when she placed her hands on her hips, they knew this meant trouble.

"Whatever it is you are talking about out here, finish it, then come in for supper," Tamara said as she straightened her apron.

"There will be no talk of war at my table."

For a moment, the two Cherokee hung their heads low. They would not sort out why humans create a cycle of vengeance on this day. Both agreed that only war, death, and time would change.

***

In the progression of time, War Eagle's journey came to a halt in a place named Tahlequah. He met the love of his life; Tamara became his wife; life was changed for the warrior.

For his friend, Little Bear, time had not been so kind. Many moons had passed; many stars had been wished upon; many dreams of Polly had come to him.

Often it seemed as though time stood still for Little Bear.

Pressing his half of Polly's red ribbon to his lips, he knew that only when the ribbon became whole again would time be kind to him.

Could it be that only the passing of time would heal Little Bear's broken heart?

Great men take advantage of time. So it was with Sam Houston. Healing from the wound he suffered in the battle at San Jacinto, Sam Houston returned to Texas to be elected president of the Republic of Texas.

Serving as president from October 22, 1836, to December 16, 1838, he was able to protect the

Cherokee Indian so they could remain on their land in Texas. When new leaders controlled the militia in Texas, War Eagle and most Cherokee were driven from their homes and the beloved Cherokee Chief Bowles was killed.

Mr. Houston remained in Texas as a representative in the Texas House of Representatives. Although his position in government had changed, Sam Houston still had the power to get some things done.

Seeking his help, missionaries from the United States sought to establish the first private Christian educational institution west of the Mississippi River. Friendships formed between Mr. Houston and several of the leaders of the movement. Accepting an invitation to attend a dinner party given by R. E. B. Baylor, Mr. Houston arrived to be greeted by the most beautiful woman he had ever seen.

When Mr. Baylor made introductions—"Sam Houston, I would like to present Miss Margaret Moffette Lea"—time stopped for the great Sam Houston.

By the end of that evening, Sam Houston was sure of one thing. He was going to marry that young lady from Alabama, Miss Margaret.

Formal meetings were always arranged with Miss Margaret and her father. It was at one of these meetings that Sam Houston asked Mr. Lea for permission to marry his daughter.

Getting an answer of yes from Mr. Lea—or even from Miss Margaret—was not going to happen without the approval of another person, however.

There was just one thing to do: travel to Alabama to meet Mother.

Stories of Sam Houston's gallant service to the Republic of Texas had reached Mrs. Lea's ears long before his arrival at her doorstep. Treating him with respect, she was not hesitant to have him as her son-in-law.

Still, Miss Margaret had one other person who must approve of her husband selection. As they were on their way to visit her best friend, Margaret had a love story to tell her fiancé.

Describing her friend, Polly, and Polly's friend, Little Bear, tears filled her eyes as she revealed the legend of the red ribbon.

Listening to her every word intently, Sam Houston already knew this story well. Margaret had no way of knowing that.

Once the carriage stopped in front of the substantial farmhouse, a figure bounded across the lawn and into Margaret's arms.

After the excited women regained their composure, Margaret said, "Polly, I have brought someone for you to meet."

Polly reached out her hand to him. "You must be Sam Houston."

In one hand, he took her small, warm hand; with his other hand, he caressed it. Looking into her dark-black eyes, only one word could describe the mighty Sam Houston: mesmerized.

Margaret giggled. "Sam, you can let go of her hand now." Embarrassed, Sam let go of Polly's hand.

"I'm sorry, I just…"

"It's all right, dear," Margaret assured him. "All men react to Polly in that way. I'm not jealous. I'm used to it."

After Polly's husband was introduced, Sam was in conversation with him, but it was Polly who controlled his attention. Her beauty, her graceful ways, her soft yet strong voice, her playful laugh—never in his entire life had he seen such a truly beautiful person.

The evening grew late; Margaret placed her head on Sam's shoulder as they rode in the carriage.

"So, dear, what do you think of my friend, Polly?" Margaret yawned as she asked.

"What do I think? I think she is a good friend, and she has a very nice husband," was his safe answer.

His thoughts were entirely different, though. There was no doubt in his mind that this lovely creature was none other than Little Bear's Polly.

It was not until they returned to Texas that Sam said, "Margaret, I have something to tell you. You see, there was this Cherokee Indian boy who worked for me and became my friend. His name is Little Bear."

Margaret stood spellbound as Sam continued, "Little Bear has half of Polly's red ribbon. I know because I have seen it. Also, I listened to the story many times. Little Bear told how he cut the red ribbon in half, left one half tied to her cabin door, and he keeps the other half in his pocket."

Oh no, now he had made her angry.

"Why did you not tell her? You should have told her," she scolded Sam.

"Not my place," said Sam.

"Polly still has her half of the red ribbon. While you were talking to her husband, we were in her bedroom. She keeps the red ribbon in a drawer of a little table that stands next to her bed. I saw it," Margaret said. "Sam, what are we going to do about this?"

"I say we do nothing. In time, they may find each other," he replied. "The time is now for us, my lovely Margaret. Are you too angry with me to be my wife?"

All sense of disagreement melted away. "Yes, Sam Houston, yes, I will be you wife."

In May 1840, the ringing of wedding bells brought happiness to the life of War Eagle and Sam Houston.

***

Wandering deep into the wood, Little Bear pondered his life's vision. Without clarity of reason in his life, Little Bear seemed to be crossing a bridge from his dream world into a world of reality.

On one hot summer day, he rested beside the trunk of an old oak tree. Keen hearing brought the voice of the spirits on the breeze through the trees.

Closing his eyes, he felt the coolness. With a sense of comfort, remembering the land he grew up on and the beliefs of his people, Little Bear sought to walk upon the wind and let it carry him where he needed to be and show him what was in his heart.

The wisdom of the spirits must overshadow the tragedies of losing his parents, the plight of his people, and the heartache of Polly.

Although his journey had not been what he expected or wanted it to be, he knew that he must be at peace with it. His path forward must be of a new vision. He must enjoy every day of life that he is given.

Between the day becoming night, Little Bear walked out of the woods and into his future.

Little Bear had no way of knowing that Sam Houston had found his Polly.

Among the flowers that grew along the riverbank, she knelt to pick some and placed them in her basket.

"Hello," he said quietly. He did not want to startle her.

She still jumped at the sound of his voice, knocking over her basket of flowers.

"I am so sorry," he said. "Here, let me help you with those." "I can do it myself, mister. You be on your way," she said.

If he heard her, he wasn't listening as he gathered flowers to fill her basket.

Standing, she picked up the basket, at the same time taking her first look at him.

Seconds, minutes, hours...how long did they look into each other's eyes?

A romance blossomed, with many evenings being shared with the young woman's mother and brother. Also, dinners were enjoyed with War Eagle and Tamara. From the time Little Bear introduced her—"War Eagle, Tamara, I would like for you to meet Window Bird—War Eagle could see that the love of Window Bird was the key that opened the gate to his friend's happiness.

It is not clear which one was the most excited, War Eagle or Little Bear, but it was time for the wedding.

The crowd stretched from the holy circle, over the riverbank, into the woods and meadow beyond. Seemed everyone in Tahlequah knew this couple. The bride was known to be loving toward everyone. She was small in stature; her long black hair reached down her back to her waist. The most amazing thing was that her eyes were as blue as the sky.

Many knew the schoolteacher, Little Bear. Few knew the story of his life. The only thing that mattered was that on this day, he was the groom.

In part, here is the sermon delivered by the Cherokee minister:

On this day, the spirits of Window Bird and Little Bear join in their journey together. Let us pray they will always walk the path of the Great Spirit. Hold true to a sense of humility, kindness, wonder, and respect for all living things. May they follow the sacred trail of those who have come before them and those yet to come.

In conclusion, the minister said, "In the circle of life, I now join Window Bird Jacobs and Little Bear..." He stammered, embarrassed to ask. Silence was broken when a voice from within the crowd spoke loud and clear, "Houston."

Eyes followed the sound as the crowd parted to make a path for the man, who made his way forward. Before Little Bear could turn to see, War Eagle whispered in his ear, "Houston, it is Sam Houston."

Standing just behind Little Bear, Mr. Houston said to the minister, "Little Bear Houston, he is my son."

For the minister, the only thing left to say was, "I now pronounce you man and wife."

Turning to Mr. Houston, Little Bear embraced him, holding on until Houston said, "Kiss your bride, Little Bear. Kiss your bride."

The celebration began with War Eagle inviting Mr. Houston to join family and close friends at Tamara and his home.

When Tamara was introduced to Sam Houston as Little Bear's sister, Houston immediately responded, "Oh, I am so sorry. I didn't know a family member was present. I was understanding that Little Bear had no family here. Guess I was out of line giving Little Bear my name."

Tamara assured Mr. Houston that she was not offended. "If anyone could take our father's place, it is you, Mr. Houston. We will be proud to share the name of such a great man."

Little Bear had a question for his friend, War Eagle. "Is this your doing? How did you get Mr. Houston to come here?"

Houston spoke first. "Let me answer that. He told me if I didn't come to your wedding, you boys would never fight for me again."

They all joined in laughter over that. During the many hours of conversation between Sam Houston, War Eagle, and Little Bear, Mr. Houston could not bring himself to tell his boys that he had seen and met Polly.

Little Bear was married to another, as was Polly. But something made Sam Houston and his wife, Margaret, wonder. Polly kept her half of the red ribbon in the drawer of her nightstand, and, yes, on the day

Houston said good-bye to Little Bear, he noticed something in his shirt pocket. Surely, it was the red ribbon.

Three weddings for three friends:
War Eagle marries Tamara.
Sam Houston marries Margaret.
Little Bear marries Window Bird.
Time changes everything.

CHAPTER
TWENTY-FOUR
Happiness Found

Laughter often filled the classroom as War Eagle entered wearing traditional Cherokee medicine-man clothing and doing tricks of the medicine man and of Cherokee warriors.

Tamara, the funny man's wife, didn't think his tricks were funny and ordered such activity out into the schoolyard, especially when bow and arrow were involved.

"I am the teacher here. You and my students will do as I say," scolded Tamara.

"Yes, my dear, you are so cute when you give the orders," War Eagle teased.

Enrollment in the school was so high that new classrooms were being built. Caring for the children of

Tahlequah was the second priority for War Eagle; his first priority was keeping Tamara happy.

As happiness filled their home and schoolhouse, so did it enter the hearts of many Cherokee.

The domestic strife within the Cherokee Nation seemed to be ending. All were hopeful of entering a period of peace and prosperity.

Sam Houston was once again elected president of Texas and negotiated peace treaties with the remaining Texas Cherokee. In Tahlequah and the Indian Territory, the Cherokee adopted more and more elements of white culture and governed themselves more as the United States did.

In summer 1842, into Tahlequah walked a man of whom Jack Kilpatrick wrote: "Sequoyah was always in the wilderness.

He walked about, but he was not a hunter. I wonder what he was looking for."

From the yard of the schoolhouse, War Eagle saw him walking down the road. War Eagle could see the man looked tired and thirsty.

"Come sit under the shade tree while I get you drink of water," War Eagle offered.

The stranger sat down on the grass, reached into his pocket, and pulled out a smoking pipe. He did not ask permission to smoke. He proceeded to ready the pipe and light it for smoking.

Not disturbed by this behavior, War Eagle had seen his Uncle Bowles do the same thing. Only difference, this was some strange pipe this fellow had.

Best find out who this guy is, thought War Eagle. As security guard for the school, he had a need to know.

"What is your name, mister?" No need to be polite. "I am Sequoyah. I thank you for the water. Is this the schoolhouse?"

War Eagle almost fell over. Could it be the "talking leaves" man? "Excuse me for my manners," War Eagle said, reaching out to shake hands. "I am War Eagle, nephew of Chief Bowles. I am so proud to meet you.

"Yes, yes this is the schoolhouse of Tahlequah. My wife is a teacher here, and I help keep up the place." War Eagle paused to catch his breath.

"And to guard against strangers like me," Sequoyah said, chuckling.

After some more conversation, War Eagle walked this great man of history into the schoolhouse.

169

It was the beginning of a several-day visit. He talked with the students and was a guest in the home of War Eagle and Tamara.

Somewhere between sixty-five and eighty years old at the time, Sequoyah's journey west had two purposes: to encourage usage of his syllabary among Native American tribes and to look for the Cherokee in Mexico to invite them to rejoin their tribes, Men in the Cherokee Nation.

A year after the time spent with Sequoyah, War Eagle received word that Sequoyah had succeeded in finding the Cherokee in Mexico, but he died and was buried there among them.

Unfortunately, Sequoyah's visit to Tahlequah was not shared with Little Bear and his wife, Window Bird. They had found happiness in another place.

They understood that home is something that changes as life changes, and searching for home in one place only to find that home was somewhere completely different was the story of Little Bear's journey.

As a young boy, Little Bear's home was the homeland of the Eastern Cherokee. Memories of his life there with his family and sweetheart, Polly, would never be lost to him, even as he crossed the river into the world beyond.

Little Bear was recognized as a skilled teacher of both English and Cherokee, and the state of Missouri, having approved a public school system in 1839, was in need of teachers.

The silent dream of the young couple, wishing, hoping to create the spirit of home, became real as they reached a new land. The way of life they brought to that land would become the story of their new home as one.

War Eagle and Tamara, living in Tahlequah, found Missouri a wonderful place to visit.

Happiness was found by this family of four: War Eagle and Tamara, Little Bear's sister; and Little Bear and Window Bird.

CHAPTER

TWENTY-FIVE

In the Blink of an Eye

How is it that life can be so perfect, and then, without warning, everything changes? Can it be just the ebb and flow of time itself?

Feeling that something was wrong, War Eagle and Tamara loaded their wagon with supplies from Tahlequah.

"I know my brother will be happy to get new books for his school," said Tamara.

"And Window Bird will be grateful for the garden tools and to see me," War Eagle said, looking for a reaction from his wife.

He got only a swish of her hands in the air as she laughed.

172

The trip began as usual, but upon crossing from Oklahoma into Missouri, it became apparent that something was terribly wrong.

The land of pure rivers, pastures, forest, and fertile fields were now devoid of man and horse tending the soil. No old men fished in the creek; no cattle grazed in the pastures; no children ran and laughed in the field of wildflowers. There were only the faint sounds of nature in the forest.

Standing on a high hill, among a stand of oak and hickory trees, with open fields around it was a house, a cabin, the home of Little Bear and Window Bird.

As the sun set on another day, there was no greeting. No Little Bear running down the road catching a ride on the wagon. No Window Bird calling from the front porch, "Come on in the house, out of this summer heat."

There was no glass of fresh lemonade.

War Eagle asked Tamara to stay in the wagon while he went inside the house. Of course, she could not do this; she beat him to the front door.

Opening the door, Little Bear fell into her arms. As they embraced, it was hard for either one to speak.

"My brother, my brother, tell me," she said. Then she saw past him. Window Bird lay in the bed, covered with quilts.

"Window Bird is sick?" Tamara quickly went to her bedside.

War Eagle guided his best friend out onto the front porch and sat him down in the rocker.

"I'm here, my brother. What can we do?" War Eagle had to be strong. This was a different kind of battle for the warrior.

From across the sea, ships sailed, carrying immigrants to the land of America. In the year 1849, the discovery of gold in California brought many of these immigrants into Missouri, bound for the gold fields of California.

When the streamer Alton pulled into Saint Louis, Missouri, it carried a disease that would kill thousands of people. On the ship's journey upriver from New Orleans, five children and one woman had died. The deaths were attributed to dysentery; but it is most likely that they succumbed to cholera.

It can be assumed that the germs of cholera were carried by crew and passengers disembarking and making their way to the homes of family and friends.

Window Bird became ill after returning from a trip to Saint Louis to purchase sewing materials that were brought into port on ships that carried diseased immigrants.

Little Bear cried as he told War Eagle, "The doctor says it is not good news. My wife is afflicted with the cholera. The doctor will do what he can, but she is dying."

All the days and nights of loving kinship, prayers, and doctor's care could not save Window Bird. Death was the only thing that would alleviate the suffering.

"Tonight, leave my window open," were her last words. The darkness came. The spirit of Window Bird passed through the open window to join the wind.

Without fear or consideration of quarantine, Tamara had embraced her beloved sister-in-law, often lifting her tiny body to care for her.

No medicine or prayers saved Tamara from this deadly scourge. Church bells tolled for two souls. Two best friends mourned the loss of a wife and sister. From tears to anger to tears again. How could they live through this?

"I killed my sister," Little Bear said in anguish. "I should have stopped her at my door and not let her tend to Window Bird."

"There is no fault with you," replied War Eagle. "I told Tamara to stay in the wagon. She didn't listen to me, and you know she would not do as you say."

"I know; my sister had a mind of her own. My heart is broken." Tears rolled down Little Bear's cheeks.

After the funeral of Tamara, the two friends walked down the hill to the creek, where so many times they had seen Window Bird and Tamara sitting on a rock, dangling their bare feet in the cool, clear water. Sounds of chatter and oh, so much laughter had drifted in the breeze to their husbands' ears.

Remembering the face of his grandmother, that of his Uncle Bowles, and his mother's love, although he could not remember her face, War Eagle broke the silence.

"Do you think Tamara and Window Bird are now with others who have gone before?" was War Eagle's question.

"I do not know the answer to your question," said Little Bear. "If it comforts you to think so, so be it."

"My father, Sky Walker, believed there was a place on the other side of the sky. He left me, searching for that place. I just wonder if one must die before he finds the other side of the sky."

Another question from War Eagle that his friend could not answer.

From the first time he saw her on the muddy streets of Tahlequah, War Eagle had loved her. By some miracle,

Tamara was also the sister who had been lost to Little Bear.

At the end of the road from Texas to Oklahoma, both War Eagle and Little Bear had found love and their place of home.

The glow of the setting sun soon faded. Wrapping the end of a long stick with layers of cloth and tying the cloth securely, Little Bear handed it to War Eagle.

Little Bear then set fire to the cloth just before War Eagle tossed it onto the roof of the little house on the hill.

As the flames engulfed the home, the two friends rode off into the night.

It was as if all was lost in the blink of an eye.

Historical Facts

- **Cholera Epidemic 1849**: Cholera is a bacterial infection that can kill a healthy person within hours. It is believed to have been transmitted by European immigrants to the United States. It first reached Missouri in 1832, killing hundreds; then, in 1849, total deaths were in the thousands. In 1884, Dr. Robert Koch isolated the bacillus that causes the disease. Until Koch's discovery, the "bad air" theory for the spread of cholera still prevailed. The establishment of sewer systems and a healthy supply of drinking water was the medicine needed. It was not until Dr. Koch's discovery that major cities, such as Saint Louis, Missouri, could rid themselves of this deadly scourge.

- **Missouri**: The United States acquired Missouri from France in 1803 as part of the Louisiana Purchase. In 1821, Missouri was admitted to the union. The Mississippi River forms the state's eastern border. The Missouri River forms its northwestern border. The Missouri River flows into the Mississippi River. The invention of the steamboat and the use of these boats on the Mississippi and Missouri rivers made Missouri a center of commerce and a gateway to the West for immigrants.

- **Tahlequah**: City in Cherokee County, Oklahoma. A settlement as early as 1832, it was founded as a capital of the original Cherokee Nation in 1838. The Eastern and Western Cherokee joined their governments at Tahlequah in 1839.

- **Indian Territory**: The region stretching from the state boundaries of Arkansas, Missouri, and Iowa to the one hundredth meridian, about 300 miles at the widest point. In 1830, the United States government promised this land would be the permanent home for Indian tribes of the southeastern United States. It was a promise "as long as the grass grows and the waters run." Five Indian tribes, the Cherokees, Chickasaws, Choctaws, Creeks, and Seminoles, were sent to this territory. It was meant to be occupied only by Indians, but that changed years later when on April 22, 1889, white homesteaders were allowed to cross the border and stake land claims. On November 16, 1907, this land became the US state of Oklahoma. Oklahoma is a Choctaw Indian word meaning "red people."

- **Trail of Tears**: Term given to the mass exodus of the Cherokee when they were forced to move westward. Because some Cherokee refused to go west on their own, United States government soldiers rounded up families and took them to internment camps in preparation for the journey westward. With little food and unsanitary conditions at these hastily built stockades, many Cherokee died. On the 800-mile trip, many died from disease and inadequate food and blankets. They were driven at a cruel pace. Soldiers did not even allow them to bury their dead properly.

About 4,000 Cherokee died, almost a quarter of their total.

- **Sequoyah**: (1767–1843) English name, George Gist or Guess. A Cherokee silversmith who, in 1821, completed his independent creation of a Cherokee syllabary, making reading and writing in Cherokee possible. This was the only time in recorded history that a member of an illiterate people independently created an effective writing system. After seeing its worth, the Cherokee Nation rapidly began to use his syllabary and officially adopted it in 1825. The Native Americans referred to Sequoyah's correspondence as "talking leaves." The Cherokee Phoenix, the first newspaper of the Cherokee, was printed with text in English and Cherokee. "Walk-A-Bout" was the name given to Sequoyah after he walked to the new Cherokee territory in Oklahoma. His journey had two purposes: to unite the splintered Cherokee Nation and to create a syllabary for use among Native American tribes.

  A gravesite near a freshwater spring in Coahuila, Mexico, may be Sequoyah's. Jack Kilpatrick wrote, "Sequoyah was always in the wilderness. He walked about, but he was not a hunter. I wonder what he was looking for."

- **Texas History**:

1842: War with Mexico continued. Although Texas governed itself, Mexico refused to recognize its independence.

1845: On February 28, 1845, the United States passed a bill that authorized the United States to annex the Republic of Texas, and on March 1, United States President John Tyler signed the bill.

1846–1848: The war with Mexico would now be fought between the United States and Mexico. On April 25, 1846, American troops moved into a disputed area between Texas and Mexico. The Mexican army moved in also, and the United States declared war. In March 1847, an American force under General Winfield Scott landed at Vera Cruz, Mexico. Within a few weeks, the capital, Mexico City, surrendered. The treaty of Guadalupe Hidalgo gave the United States all the territory that is now included in Utah, Nevada, and California, and parts of Arizona, New Mexico, Colorado, and Wyoming. Postwar Texas grew rapidly as migrants poured into the cotton lands of the state.

- **Pottery and clothing**: Native American women made pottery. They made their pottery by coiling long strings of clay, squeezing them together, and then smoothing out the rough coils. Pottery was used for cooking, eating, and storing seeds for crops. Animal skins were tanned to make clothing. During the 1800s, interactions between Indian tribes white Europeans brought many cultural changes to the Texas Cherokee. The Indians bartered with white people for cloth and items to make clothing. They began to dress in Anglo-American style in the 1800s.

Presidents of the United States from 1841–1850

- **William Henry Harrison**: b. 2/9/1773, d. 4/4/1841, term of office: one month in 1841. The ninth president of the United States. As governor of the New Indiana Territory, he negotiated treaties with the Indians that gave settlers millions of acres of land. In 1811, Harrison led US troops to defeat the Indian resistance in the Battle of Tippecanoe. Then, in 1812, he was a US general leading his troops to defeat the British and their Indian allies. He served in the US House of Representatives, the Ohio State Senate, the US Senate, and as minister to Colombia. "Old Tip," he was called as he ran for US president. He and his vice-president ran on the slogan, "Tippecanoe and Tyler, too." On the day, he was inaugurated, Harrison insisted on standing in the drizzle wearing no hat or coat. He caught a cold that turned into pneumonia. He died one month later. Vice President John Tyler became the next president of the United States.

- **John Tyler**: b. 3/29/1790, d. 1/18/ 1862, term of office: 1841–1845. In 1825, he was elected governor of the state of Virginia. From 1827 to 1836, he was a US Senator from Virginia. As president of the United States in 1842, he ended the Second Seminole War. Improving relations between the United States and Great Britain, he settled a long-standing border dispute between the state of Maine and Canada. As a member of the Whig Party, he was expected to go along with Congress's decision to create a new national bank. Tyler believed that each state should give consent to open a branch of the bank. After Tyler's second veto of a Congress's bill, his entire cabinet resigned, except for Secretary of State Daniel Webster. Tyler then became "a man without a party." Without the support of a party, Tyler could not run for a full term as president. Perhaps his greatest achievement was signing the resolution annexing Texas on March 1, 1845. Texas became a state ten months later.

- **James Knox Polk**: b. 11/2/1795, d. 6/15/1849, term of office: 1845–1849. He was the eleventh president of the United States. A lawyer, he was elected in 1835 to the US House of Representatives from the state of Tennessee. In 1839, he was elected governor of Tennessee. He was one of the strongest presidents of the nineteenth century. He believed in Manifest Destiny—the right of the United States to expand westward across the continent. He finalized the annexation of Texas to the United States, and then he urged Congress to declare war on Mexico. As a result of the Mexican War (1846–1848), the United States acquired what are now California, Nevada, Utah, and part of Arizona, New Mexico, Colorado, and Wyoming. Polk also settled a controversy with Britain over the Oregon Territory. The two countries agreed to set the northern boundary of Oregon at the forty-ninth parallel. Polk also reduced the tariff-tax on goods brought into the country and reestablished an independent treasury. Polk's four years in office exhausted him. He died three months after leaving office.

- **Zachary Taylor**: b. 11/24/1784, d. 7/9/1850, term of office: 1849–1850. The twelfth president of the United States served forty years in the US Army. Known as "Old Rough and Ready," he fought in the War of 1812, the Seminole Indian War, and the War with Mexico. The California gold rush of 1849 was a major event during Zachary Taylor's term in office. Thousands of prospectors struggled across the country to seek their fortune.

PART FOUR

CHAPTER TWENTY-SIX
New Direction

With wind whirling the rain into a violent downpour, War Eagle and Little Bear rode out of Missouri, struggling to stay in their saddles.

"I can't do this," said War Eagle. Being a brave warrior, he had never even thought these words when given a difficult task. Now, he must return to Tahlequah without his wife. He must return to the home where he and Tamara had spent years of happiness.

"We will share our grief. I have lost my sister for the second time. Why did the river not take her? Why did the cholera do what the river could not?" Little Bear wiped tears from his cheeks.

Before entering Tahlequah, the friends found a trading post where they shed their clothing and dressed themselves in traditional Indian buckskin shirts, pants, and boots.

The storekeeper asked them what he should do with their old clothing. Without hesitation, both Cherokee responded, "Burn them!"

Before reaching the house, they found Billy, Little Bear's brother-in-law, Window Bird's brother. Billy had become a lawyer and had an office in Tahlequah.

The three men gave each other strength to empty out the house, go to the schoolhouse for a service in honor of their beloved teacher, Tamara, and in appreciation of War Eagle, Little Bear, and Window Bird. The three men gave each other strength to rest the souls of their loved ones.

"What will you do now?" Billy asked War Eagle.

"Billy," War Eagle responded, "I want you to sell the house and donate the money to the school. You ask what I will do. I don't know. I am lost."

Hearing the conversation, Little Bear spoke up.

"Then we shall be lost together."

"Perhaps we will do as my father, Sky Walker, did: search for the other side of the sky," War Eagle stated.

"I do not know where your father is," said Little Bear, "but we do have another father. It is time we seek him for a new direction."

Wasting little time, they said their good-byes, saddled their horses, and called into the Oklahoma wind, "Sam Houston and Texas, here we come!"

Their first day out of Tahlequah, they stopped at Fort Gibson.

When they entered the front gate, the soldiers seemed to pay little attention to the two Cherokee. Their question to the guard at the gate was, "Where can we find the horse stable?"

The guard directed them to the stable, adding, "You boys can bed down with your horses in the stable, since it is late. Don't go wandering around the fort."

"Yes, sir," War Eagle replied. The stable keeper was an Indian man. He showed them a place to sleep that night, repeating the guard's statement, "Don't go wandering around the fort tonight."

Restless was not a strong enough word to use for War Eagle's condition. As soon as Little Bear fell asleep, War Eagle walked out of the stable.

Soon, several soldiers approached him. They offered War Eagle a drink of their whiskey. It was party time for the soldiers. Pouring whiskey into an Indian and then taunting him and laughing at him. What fun.

After a few drinks, War Eagle did not mind. His troubled mind relaxed, and he found himself in a peaceful place.

At sunrise, Little Bear woke to find his friend missing. It did not take him but few steps to find War Eagle slumped over a hitching post outside the stable. Before Little Bear reached War Eagle, he could smell him. Without a word being said, he knew exactly what had happened. Little Bear had been down that road before.

With a bucket of water, Little Bear cleaned his friend up. The only things coming from War Eagle were groans and the statement, "My head hurts."

Little Bear knew what he had to do. First, get some black coffee into his friend; and second, leave the fort and get War Eagle away from the soldiers.

With horses saddled and War Eagle sober, the two decided to get some supplies from the general store before leaving the fort.

Upon entering the store, they saw a big, burly, white man trying to explain to the clerk what he wanted.

Angrily, the clerk shouted, "You German, speak English. I can't understand a word you are saying."

War Eagle and Little Bear were ready to defend the German. They had heard his language spoken in Missouri; it was not strange to them.

Walking up behind the German, War Eagle said to the clerk, "Looks to me like the items the man wants are laying on your counter. What kind of talking does he need to do?

"Now, my friend here can name all the items plain and simple in your language. Do you want him to tell you in Cherokee or English or some other tongue? I suggest you just wait on the German."

With War Eagle standing just inches away from the clerk, the German began to walk toward the door.

Little Bear raised his voice, calling, "Come back here, Mr. German. You need to get your things."

It was amazing how quickly the attitude of the store clerk changed. Timidly, he went about helping the German with his purchases. Then, as he helped the two Indians, no words were spoken.

"You got a wagon, mister?" asked War Eagle. "I will help you carry your stuff out."

It was strange to see the German, a man of such strong stature, so humble in his appreciation. You didn't have to speak German to understand that the words he repeated meant "Thank you."

The German was a man from a land beyond the rivers, the mountains, the ocean; his looks and language were so very different. Cherokee Indian and German, their heritages were worlds apart.

But because of the gift of humanity, they were no longer strangers.

CHAPTER
TWENTY-SEVEN
Wagon Train

Is it fate, or that ebb and flow of life, that a happenstance meeting determines ones destiny?

Sometimes actions have no reason, as it was with War Eagle and Little Bear, who followed the German and his wagon.

Looking back, now and again, the German seemed happy that the two Indians were with him. It was not until they reached the crest of a hill that the wagon, the German, the horses, War Eagle, and Little Bear came to a complete halt.

It was a remarkable sight. Never before in their lives had the Cherokee friends seen such a thing. A train of covered wagons formed three different circles; an ample number of horses grazed in a field nearby. From what War Eagle could see, the men, women, and children were all white people, and there were enough of them to make up a village.

The German motioned for the Cherokee to come with him. "You go find out what it is," Little Bear said to War Eagle. "What? Do you want to get me killed?" War Eagle had a better idea. "You go find out. I'll stay on the hill."

Before the decision was made, a white man rode up on his horse and spent a few minutes talking to the German.

The little voice in War Eagle's head said to him, "Ride man, ride," but he would not leave his friend, who was moving closer and closer to the conversation between the German and the rider.

He was not sure of what words were spoken, but shortly, War Eagle relaxed as he could see the white man was friendly.

"You boys Indian scouts looking for work?" The man then introduced himself. "I am Vic Thompson, wagon master. I am looking for a good Indian scout to join my wagon train."

War Eagle and Little Bear remained still in their saddles, staring at the scene below.

"Never saw a wagon train before?" asked Thompson. War Eagle backed away and let his friend do the talking. "No, sir, not out here," explained Little Bear.

"I know some wagons like that come across the big river, but never seen anything like this. Where they going out here?"

"Going? Going west to California. The people on this wagon train plan to get rich. I'll pay you good money to ride with us to California," the wagon master said, trying to make a deal.

"Well, what do you say, War Eagle?" Little Bear asked. "Say about what?"

"Going west with the German and the wagon train," explained Little Bear.

"Why would we do a thing like that? You know and I know that neither of us knows nothing about being a scout. Not even what the word means," War Eagle said, sounding as though his answer was no.

Little Bear was not ready to give up on the deal, but he could see that his friend was focused on going to Texas, not to this faraway place called California.

Realizing that the two Cherokee were about to ride away, the German yelled out, "Gold!"

"What did he say?" asked War Eagle.

"Mr. Vic Thompson, what does he mean, gold?" Little Bear questioned.

"That is why we are going to California. It is a land filled with gold," said the wagon master.

The face of the German lit up. "Gold," he repeated, "Gold."

CHAPTER

TWENTY-EIGHT

"Gold!"

Come morning, War Eagle and Little Bear found themselves having breakfast with the German and his wife. Having spent the night bedded down beneath the German's wagon, they were awakened by the voice of a woman. The only word they understood was "coffee."

She was a pleasant woman and intent on feeding them until they were well awake and would not be hungry for some time.

With the sun rising in the east, the encampment came alive.

Mothers could be heard calling their children; men called their horses; none of these morning activities was done quietly.

Before the Cherokee friends could adjust to the situation, Vic Thompson, the wagon master showed up.

"You boys ready to ride?" he said, greeting them.

The friends looked at each other. War Eagle was first to speak. "We go where the German goes."

"I think he means the German's wife. The food in his stomach makes up his mind," Little Bear teased.

"OK, then. Get your horses saddled, and when the wagons line up, meet me in front of the first wagon in line." The wagon master was pleased.

Still not sure of what they were supposed to do but remembering the light in the German's eyes when he said the word "gold," War Eagle said, "If it is scout they want to call us, then we will be the best Indian scouts we can be." War Eagle was eager to get started.

When the wagons lined up, they stretched a mile long. It was probably the longest wagon train ever to cross the country. As part of this wagon train, the Cherokee friends became part of the "forty-niners," the term used for those seeking gold fields in 1849.

The German and other immigrants from all around the world came to America seeking land and gold. They fought for their freedom to have both.

War Eagle and Little Bear were leaving their sorrows behind, as others left their homes and countries to join this wagon train on a journey to the gold region of California and make their dreams come true.

Gold was buried in the sands that skirt the shores of rolling rivers, they were told. Gold was in the ravines that form from the torrential waters; gold was in the waters' rippling run; gold was bedded in the brooklets; all was free for the taking.

Ignoring this thing they called "gold fever," and not knowing the meaning of "Indian scout," War Eagle and Little Bear were excellent students of the wagon master. After their first encounter with some Western Indians, the two Cherokee realized their job was to negotiate passage and assistance from the native people.

War Eagle was the better of the two at using the Western Indian sign language. The first time Little Bear tried his hand at it, the entire group of Apache

Indians laughed at him and hurriedly rode away.

War Eagle asked Little Bear to show him what he had done, but Little Bear turned red in the face.

"No, I am not showing you nothing," he stubbornly replied. "Well," said War Eagle, "you best leave the signing to me." "Got rid of them, didn't I?" Little Bear now laughed.

More and more, the people of the wagon train grew to trust War Eagle's dealings with the Western Indians.

Dreams often faded as the dreamers made their way across the plains. Hills, hollows, mudholes, wet prairie, rivers to cross with no bridges, and bad roads or no roads at all led many people to turn back, swearing.

Months into the journey, babies had been born, several of the older people had died, and often the entire wagon train had to band together to confront obstacles. No, there was no turning back.

Embracing the task of helping these people, War Eagle not only provided security from the Indians of the West, but he also used his muscles for working at whatever needed to be done.

Little Bear used his teaching skills. Soon, his evenings were occupied teaching the English language to Germans and learning the German language from them.

Along with the English classes, Little Bear taught Cherokee, telling stories of his people, the Native Americans.

Everyone's favorite was the story of Sequoyah. A bet was made with the people of the wagon train.

"The first people in California to use the Cherokee alphabet will be you," Little Bear said, sure that he would win this wager.

Trusting and understanding each other, War Eagle, Little Bear, the German, and others formed a bond of friendship.

There was just one thing about which the German and several others were curious, and it led them to question War Eagle.

"What is the thing in Little Bear's pocket? Looks like an old red ribbon. What does he use it for?"

"He uses it for his heart," said War Eagle.

In clear English, the German said, "How use thing in his pocket for heart?"

Leaning close to the German, War Eagle whispered loudly enough for the others to hear, "You leave that thing in his pocket alone, if you want to keep your scalp."

The red ribbon was not mentioned again.

Four months passed, and the wagon train continued its journey.

CHAPTER
TWENTY-NINE
Finding California

"Praise God from whom all blessings flow." Raising his voice, the preacher spoke to the weary travelers as they gathered round.

The sun rose in the east, its rays filtering through the clouds and embracing all those who endured this journey, nurturing their souls and the land that lay before them.

Many had lost love ones; most had lost hope. On this Sunday morning, excitement filled the air. The dream was still alive. They had found California!

"We have reached the Territory of California," the wagon master told the people of the wagon train. "Do you want to find the gold fields?"

A loud "yes" reverberated around the wagon train. Shouting continued for several minutes until Mr. Thompson quieted them down. "All right, then, prepare your wagons; ready your horses; it's going to be a bumpy ride."

Leading the way, War Eagle motioned to turn the wagons west for a short distance, and then north. Next came a turn to the west. All they could see were mountains. Monsters that no man, wagon, or beast could climb over.

Once the Indian scout, now the trailblazer, War Eagle, seemingly out of nowhere, found a pass through the mountains. Treacherous? Yes. With renewed strength, they followed War Eagle.

With faith and courage, they worked together, pushing past all obstacles and moving forward.

As War Eagle guided the wagons, Little Bear comforted the children. "We don't need to be afraid," he told them. "Pretend we are in a tunnel. Keep looking at the light at the end of the tunnel."

Coming out of the pass, songs of joy erupted from the children. Not only had they found the light at the end of the tunnel, but before them was a sight to behold.

Many rejoiced. Others concentrated on their tasks at hand. All felt the renewal of hope and faith in their dream of finding fields of gold.

They had found California. Was this the land of gold? Dense, morning fog lifted, revealing vast green pastures, separated by rivers and creeks, and trees of all sizes bearing fruits and nuts.

To the east and to the west, mountains hugged the fertile land as though it were a womb.

Moving slowly through the valley, the wagon train was in no hurry to leave the tranquil scene.

War Eagle was taking a nap in the German's wagon. No one bothered to wake the trusted Indian scout; only Little Bear teased him at the end of the day.

As the wagons moved along, riverbanks were inviting, causing some to pause and question their belief in fields of gold.

Having been farmers in their old countries, some were satisfied that this rich valley land was their field of dreams. For them, the journey was over. They would make their own gold.

Losing a third of his wagon train to the riverside homesteaders, Mr. Thompson, the wagon master, still had a job to complete. Leaving the San Joaquin Valley behind, the remaining wagons followed the watercourse of the American River.

Exploring the basin of the American River, they found the site of Sutter's Mill—the very place where gold was first found, leading to the California gold rush.

For the people of the wagon train, it was a sight to behold. Cluttered with prospectors panning for gold, the mining camp was filled with Americans, Europeans, and Asians—a universal population, half come by land and half by sea.

Mr. Thompson collected the money that was due him, and then rode off into the sunset.

War Eagle, Little Bear, the German, and others had reached the land of gold: the field of dreams for some and devastating disappointment for many.

The German had believed the stories of finding gold nuggets on the ground and finding it in streams and riverbeds using simple techniques, such as panning.

No time was wasted. The German handed picks, pans, and shovels to War Eagle and Little Bear. He had come west to make his fortune, and the two Cherokee were going to help him do just that!

CHAPTER THIRTY
Seven Years

Wooden sidewalks lined the muddy roads; saloons and gambling palaces had sprung up on every side of the camp. Some found money; others lost it, as many prospectors could not hold on to their newfound wealth.

Working days turned into working years. War Eagle and Little Bear were known to have harvested one pound of gold in a day. The German was becoming a wealthy man. There was no sharing of profits with War Eagle and Little Bear.

Wages were promised; only small allowances were given. The German justified his holding all of the money, saying that whatever he gave to the two Indians, they would drink up or spend on other evils in the saloons and palaces.

It is true that War Eagle drank heavily and was a favorite with the women. Amazing that such a strong man could be so vulnerable. Lucky for him, he had a friend, Little Bear, who was always there to pick him up and see to it that he was ready for work the next day.

Life for the two Cherokee had become just a day-to-day existence. Complacent about their plight in life, War Eagle and Little Bear worked for the German for seven years.

During those seven years, sophisticated methods were developed to recover gold. The technological advances required significant financing. Gold companies replaced the individual miners.

Many of the prospectors began to return to where they'd come from. The ramshackle mining camps they had built were abandoned.

"My land is not for sale!" shouted the German. He had reached the promised land and had more money than he could ever spend. But it was never enough.

At the end of a cold, rainy day, War Eagle sat at the bar, drinking until his money ran out. He staggered to the door, managing to walk out into the darkness of night.

At the crack of dawn, Little Bear took charge. "Saddle both horses and get ready to ride."

"Ride to where?" War Eagle's head hurt, but he did as Little Bear said.

Within minutes, Little Bear instructed, "Saddle up. Did you pack our things?"

War Eagle questioned. "Things? What things? We have no things." Little Bear sounded impatient.

War Eagle had just one more question. "What are you going to tell the German?"

"Not telling him nothing," said Little Bear. War Eagle had to have the last word. "But maybe he would give us traveling money."

They both laughed and laughed.
Sunrise found the two friends miles away from the mining camp, leaving with no more than they came with, despite all the riches they had found.

For War Eagle and Little Bear, it was seven lost years. Resting their horses, War Eagle took a bath in the cool, clear, river water. His head no longer hurt, and for the first time in many years, he felt free.

"You know what, Little Bear?" War Eagle asked humbly. "No, what?" replied his friend.

"You know that little voice you have in your head that tells you when not to do something? I don't have one of those."

It took Little Bear a few minutes to grasp the meaning of War Eagle's confession.

"Of course you don't, but that is what you have me for."

CHAPTER THIRTY-ONE

San Francisco

Riding toward the sunset and taking a path around the town, the two Cherokee felt the breeze from the ocean water.

What a mighty sight! Screaming could be heard over the noise of the crashing waves. Did yelling release the fright of their discovery? Of course, it was War Eagle who jumped from his horse and bolted across the sandy beach, right into the foamy water.

Little Bear did notice that his friend waded only knee-deep in the water.

"Come on, Little Bear! I dare you to get your feet wet!" War Eagle called out.

After securing the horses, Little Bear accepted the challenge; only he plunged head first into the deeper water.

Without hesitation, War Eagle went in after him. Pulling his head out of the water, he yelled, "What are you doing?

Trying to drown yourself?"

Little Bear came up laughing. "No, drowning doesn't work for me. I tried that once before."

War Eagle didn't understand Little Bear's remark. He would ask about it later. Right now, all feelings of fear, sadness, heartache, and loss escaped their minds and souls. It was as though the Pacific Ocean stole them away.

On shore, they built a small fire. Wrapping themselves in their Indian blankets, they dried their clothing, ate what food they had, and sat by the fire as though waiting.

As the sun made its last peek between the sky and water, War Eagle asked, "Where does the sun go? Does it go to the other side of the sky? Does it come back as the moon? What happens out there?"

"I only know what I see," said Little Bear. "Right now, I see thousands of stars, and the quiet of darkness is peaceful."

That was probably a clue for War Eagle to stop talking, but as usual, he had to have the last word.

"Are the stars on this side of the sky? Or do they shine through the sky from the other side?"

"War Eagle, you are impossible," Little Bear said, mocking him. "Maybe someday, somewhere, a human being will be able to answer all your questions. I just know that that person is not me— not here and not now. You can stay up all night and study on all that you wonder. For me, I will be studying the back of my eyelids. My suggestion is you get rest, for tomorrow we ride again."

War Eagle asked, "Where are we going?" No answer. Of course, he had the last word. "I know. San Francisco."

***

No one seemed to pay attention to the two Cherokee Indians as they rode into town.

Asians, Europeans, people from many different nations crowded the streets. The California gold rush of 1849 had propelled the city into a period of rapid growth. In just one year, the population increased from 1,000 to 25,000, transforming it into the largest city on the West Coast at the time.

Because of the area's location as a port, the once-small settlement exploded, as the prospect of fabulous riches was so strong that crews on arriving vessels deserted and rushed off to the gold fields.

With hordes of fortune seekers streaming through the city, entrepreneurs sought to capitalize on the wealth generated by this gold rush.

Catering to the needs and tastes of the growing population, several men opened their businesses, casting their name on history.

War Eagle and Little Bear were about to meet these men of destiny. It was 1857, and War Eagle and Little Bear were there in the place called San Francisco.

Making their way through the streets, War Eagle spotted a livery stable. "What you say we park our horses and find something to eat?"

In agreement, they arranged for the horses to be cared for. Leaving the livery stable, the first store they saw had a big sign above the front doors. It read: Brannan's.

On this day, the walk from the livery stable took only a few minutes; the walk back from Brannan's store would be a long time in coming.

Approaching Brannan's store, they watched a large, heavily loaded wagon pulled by four horses arrive in front of the store, and they heard a lot of yelling. War Eagle and Little Bear were cautious.

A large, robust man waved his hands in dismay, yelling at the driver, "You are early. I have no one to off-load. What are you thinking to show up now?"

Looking back and forth from man to wagon, War Eagle suggested, "I say we help the man out. What do you say, my friend?"

Little Bear proceeded to make a deal with the man. The cost for Mr. Brannan was not going to be a problem. Supply and demand applied here. The supplies were here, the delivery was in demand. What choice did the storekeeper have?

War Eagle added to the deal, "A big hearty breakfast."

"Yes, yes, whatever it takes. Just get to work, the both of you.

I'll show you where to put everything."

After several hours of hard work and after eating the big breakfast that was part of the pay, the two Cherokee rested on the porch in front of the store.

The rest period was short. Mr. Samuel Brannan had another deal.

Holding money in his hand, he said, "You men have done an outstanding job for me today. I can give you the money you earned today, or I can hold on to it and add more at the end of the week. That is, if you agree to stay on working for me."

"No plans on staying on; just passing through," commented War Eagle.

"Only gear we have is with our horses at the livery stable. No place to hang our hats, even for tonight," added Little Bear.

"I got two rooms in back of the store," Brannan stated. "Plenty room for both of you. No charge as long as you work for me."

Remembering their situation with the German who had always kept their money, War Eagle had no trust. "Up to my friend if we stay or not," he said. "But I will be taking my pay for today."

Reason prevailed with Little Bear. "I say we take you up on your offer of your rooms with the promise of one week's work. Come Friday, we get our pay for the week."

Holding out his hand, Little Bear continued, "We will take our pay for today."

"Fine, just fine," Brannan said, handing over the money. "Free room and pay on every Friday, as long as you work for me."

As Mr. Brannan walked away, he left the two Cherokee staring at each other. What had just happened? Who made the best deal?

It took a long time to figure out the decision they made on that day.

For the first time ever, Little Bear went to the saloon with his friend, War Eagle.

CHAPTER

THIRTY-TWO

Living the Good Life

From day one, life in San Francisco changed the lifestyle of the two Cherokee friends. On the second day of working for Mr. Brannan, they were told, "You two go over to the dry goods store on California Street and ask for Mr. Levi Strauss. I spoke to him about you needing to be properly outfitted."

Mr. Levi Strauss treated them with respect, and judging by the type of clothing he provided, it seemed as though their job description was changing. Not only loading and off-loading wagons, they worked in the store selling merchandise. It had not taken Mr. Brannan long to realize that War Eagle and Little Bear were capable of doing more than that backbreaking task.

On January 9 1857, War Eagle unlocked the front door, opening the store for business. Several people waiting outside walked into the store. A sense of harmony seemed to prevail. The California sun shone on San Francisco, a town with a diverse population. The California gold rush had done this, and the melting pot included Cherokee Indians. Hardly ever were War Eagle and Little Bear asked about their Cherokee heritage.

On January 9, 1857, at 10:12 a.m., everything was normal.

At 10:13, everything changed. It took only one minute for the magnitude 8.3 earthquake to rock the world beneath their feet. Shaking violently, the entire store seemed to rise and fall; merchandise flew all over the place.

The streets soon filled with terrified people screaming, "It's the end of the world!"

War Eagle was shouting, "Little Bear, brother, where are you?"

After what seemed to be a lifetime to War Eagle, he felt a tap on his shoulder. "You looking for me?" Little Bear calmly asked.

War Eagle was not as calm as he grabbed his friend. "What is happening? Are we dead yet?"

No, they were not dead. In fact, they would survive many more of these earthquakes during their years in San Francisco.

From store clerk to teaching in the school that Mr. Brannan had opened, Little Bear even worked in the bank that Mr. Brannan opened in October 1857.

War Eagle, who possessed great strength, was put to work as a law enforcer. After a series of sensational crimes in the area, Samuel Brannan organized the San Francisco Committee of Vigilance, which functioned as a de facto police force.

Within a year, the two friends had more money than they had ever had in their lives. They now had a nice house to live in; nice suits of clothing, thanks to Levi Strauss, and best of all, they had respect from the people of San Francisco.

War Eagle no longer visited the saloons. He had a steady girlfriend named Victoria. When Little Bear asked him about marriage, he replied, "I'll marry her when you throw away that red ribbon in your pocket."

Neither one of those things were going to happen.

Watching the freedom waves of the Pacific Ocean on the western shores, they were unaware of events that were happening on the Atlantic coast of the United States, lands almost forgotten by Little Bear and never seen by War Eagle.

In 1860, news traveled from one sea across the country to the other. Once united, the country was now shattered by purpose and cause. States began to secede from the Union.

The people elected a new president, a man by the name of Abraham Lincoln. For all his good attributes, he could not stop the chaos and secession of Southern states. After his inauguration on March 4, 1861, the seceded states adopted their own government, the Confederate States of America.

The Confederacy's constitution was similar to that of the United States, but it gave more power to individual states.

Jefferson Davis was elected president of the Confederacy, which was originally based in Montgomery, Alabama, and later moved to Richmond, Virginia, the Confederate capital.

President Lincoln refused to accept the new nation; hostility prevailed, and then the inevitable war began. Davis fought for state's rights; Lincoln fought to save the Union.

The shots fired on April 12, 1861, would not only change the direction of America, but also of world history.

Showing Little Bear the California newspaper, War Eagle already knew what the news was.

"Looks like all-out war. The "rebels" (as the Confederate soldiers were called), have burned out Fort Sumter. Old "Honest Able" (as they called President Lincoln) is calling up his army to fight. You see it as I see it? Is it all-out war?"

Little Bear responded, "I say it is a sad day for the East and the West. Surely, a civil war for us all."

After sitting in silence for some time, War Eagle asked, "What do you think our father, Sam Houston, has to say about this war? California doesn't seem to be very bothered. Just wonder about Texas?"

Little Bear stated, "I hear some Californians are going east: some for the union, some for the rebels. Best we find out about Texas."

Without hesitation, War Eagle boasted, "If Texas is at war, I say, 'Father Houston, hold on. We are on our way. Fought to save your Texas once before; we can do it again.'"

The news from Sam Houston in Texas was not good. War Eagle and Little Bear had become friends during a time of war. That day, their battle cry was, "Let's Ride!"

Historical Facts

- **Fort Gibson**: Located on the Grand River (Oklahoma) just above its junction with the Arkansas River. Named for US Army Colonel (later General) George Gibson. Built in 1824 to maintain peace on the frontier of the American West.

- **Wagon Train**: A line of wagons traveling together, as one in which pioneers crossed the western plains.

- **Route to California**: From Fort Gibson, Oklahoma, wagons traveled west to Amarillo, Texas; then to Albuquerque, New Mexico; then to Flagstaff, Arizona; crossing into California at Topock on the Colorado River. At Topock, California, they turned north to the Tehachapi Mountains and followed a trail through Tehachapi Pass into Bakersfield, California. They entered the Joaquin Valley, continuing north to the gold fields located along the American River, east of San Francisco, California.

- **Gold Fields**: The California gold rush began at Sutter's Mill, near Coloma. The news of the discovery of gold brought thousands of gold seekers from all around the world. They were called the "forty-eighters" and the "forty-niners (for 1848 and 1849). Gold worth tens of billions in today's dollars was recovered, which led to great wealth for a few. However, many returned home with little more than they had started with.

- **California**: In the 1800s, California was a promised land to both Americans and immigrants. Hundreds of thousands made the difficult journey west in covered wagons. The first Europeans to settle in California were Spaniards in the 1500s. In 1822, California became part of Mexico, after Mexico won its independence from Spain. After the Mexican War with America in 1848, California became an American territory. Two years later, in 1850, after the California gold rush, it became the thirty-first state of the United States.

- **San Francisco**: The earliest archaeological evidence of human habitation of the territory that is now San Francisco dates to 3,000 BC. The Yelamo group of the Ohlone people resided in several small villages when a Spanish exploration party led by Don Gaspar de Portola arrived on November 2, 1769. It was the first documented European visit to San Francisco Bay. Seven years later, on March 28, 1776, the Spanish established the Presidio of San Francisco, followed by the Mission San Francisco de Asis (Mission Dolores).

Upon independence from Spain in 1832, the area became part of Mexico. Under Mexican rule, the mission system gradually ended and its land eventually was privatized.

In 1835, Englishman William Richardson erected the first independent homestead, near a boat anchorage at what is Portsmouth Square today. Together with Alcalde Francisco de Haro, he laid out a street plan for an expanded settlement, and the town, named Yerba Buena, began to attract American settlers. On July 7, 1846, during the Mexican-American war, Commodore John D. Sloat claimed California for the United States, and Captain John B. Montgomery arrived to claim Yerba Buena two days later. Yerba Buena was renamed San Francisco on January 30, 1847. People seeking to capitalize on the wealth generated by the gold rush pushed the population from 1,000 in 1848 to 25,000 in December 1849. By July 1, 1860, the United States census count for San Francisco was 56,802.

- **Earthquakes**: A vibration of the earth's surface that occurs after a release of energy in the earth's crust. Vast amounts of energy build up due to the friction of two tectonic plates colliding as they pass each other. A large fault, or plate boundary, runs through the West Coast of the United States. It is called the San Andreas Fault.

- **Dates of documented earthquakes** in the San Francisco area—some severe, some tremors:

January 9, 1857

February 5, 1857

March 23, 1857

September 2, 1857

September 14, 1857

October 20, 1857

November 2, 1857

November 8, 1857

November 9, 1857

December 23, 1857

December 24, 1857

January 21, 1858

April 5, 1858

August 5 18, 1858

September 12, 1858

November 26, 1858

April 27, 1859

September 22, 1859

September 24, 1859

October 5, 1859

November 19, 1859

November 27, 1859

December 1, 1859

December 24, 1859

January 1, 1860

February 9, 1860

April 5, 1860

April 16, 1860

May 25, 1860

September 23, 1860

December 21, 1860

February 2, 1861

March 23, 1861

May 4, 1861

June 13, 1861

July 3, 1861

July 4, 1861

During this period, thirty-eight earthquakes were recorded. Earthquakes are one of the most powerful natural forces on earth. v Samuel Brannan: b. 3/2/1819, d. 5/14/1889. Born in Saco, Maine, he moved to California in 1846, where he established the California Star, the first newspaper in San Francisco. In 1847, he opened a store at Sutter's Fort, near present-day Sacramento. Early in 1848, employees of John Sutter paid for goods in his store with gold they had found at Sutter's Mill, near Coloma, California. Brannan opened more stores to sell goods to the miners—his Sutter Fort store sold $150,000 in merchandise per month 1849. He began buying land in San Francisco. On October 31 1857, he opened a bank on the northeast corner of California and Montgomery Streets in San Francisco. He was known as California's first millionaire.

- **Levi Strauss**: Born Loeb Strauss in 1829 in Buttenheim, Bavaria, he was the son of a dry goods peddler. He arrived in Kentucky in 1848, learned the dry goods trade, and then went to San Francisco, California, in 1850, on the heels of the gold rush. He opened his first store in a small building on California Street. He always insisted that all of his employees call him Levi. He was active in business and cultural life in San Francisco. He sought his fortune in commerce, not gold. As Levi pushed a cart of denim for tents through the muddy San Francisco streets, a miner informed him that it was not tents, but sturdy work pants that were needed. Levi brought a swatch of denim to a local tailor, and the rest is history. The quintessential American garments were called Levi's.

- **Connecting East United States to West United States:** On March 24, 1860, the clipper ship Andrew Jackson arrived in San Francisco from New York. The trip took eighty-nine days. On April 14, 1860, the first Pony Express rider arrived in San Francisco from Saint Joseph, Missouri. On October 24, 1861, the overland telegraph was completed, which ended the Pony Express.

- **News of Crisis**: In 1861, Confederacy was the name adopted by the Southern states that seceded from the United States. The Confederacy was formed in February 1861 by South Carolina, Alabama, Florida, Georgia, Louisiana, and Mississippi. Texas joined in March; and Arkansas, North Carolina, Tennessee, and Virginia joined soon after. Some Californians, especially Southerners who had moved to California, supported seceding from the Union, but the proposal sent to Congress in Washington, DC, never came to a vote.

United States Presidents 1850–1865

- **Millard Fillmore**: b. 1/7/1800 in Locke, New York; d. 3/8/1874 in Buffalo, New York. Term of office: 1850–1853. Fillmore had been elected vice-president on the Whig ticket with Zachary Taylor. When Taylor died in office, Fillmore became the thirteenth president. Under his leadership, the Compromise of 1850, an act concerning slavery, was passed. This compromise postponed the Civil War by about ten years. His major achievement was opening up

Japanese ports to United States trade.

- **Franklin Pierce**: b. 11/23/1804 in Hillsboro, New Hampshire; d. 10/8/1869 in Concord, New Hampshire. Term of office: 1853–1857. As president, Pierce supported the Kansas-Nebraska Act (1854). It created two new territories—Kansas and Nebraska—and allowed settlers to choose whether or not they wanted slavery in the territory. His major accomplishment was the Gadsden Purchase (1853). The United States acquired a strip of land from Mexico that forms the southern part of Arizona and New Mexico. Pierce's handling of the slavery issue made him very unpopular. He was not chosen as the Democratic candidate in the 1856 presidential election.

- **James Buchanan**: b. 4/23/1791 near Mercersburg, Pennsylvania; d. 6/1/1868 in Lancaster, Pennsylvania. Term of office: 1857–1861. He served during the years just before the Civil War. When seven Southern states seceded from the Union during Buchanan's last months in office, he stated that they had no right to secede, but he had no power to stop them. With the Democratic Party split, the

Republican Party won the presidential election in 1860. In March 1861, Buchanan handed over the reins of government to Abraham Lincoln.

- **Abraham Lincoln**: b. 2/12/1809 near Hodgenville, Kentucky; d. 4/15/1865 in Washington, DC. Term of office: 1861–1865. The Civil War lasted for practically his entire time in office. Lincoln is best remembered for the Emancipation Proclamation, the speech in which he freed the slaves in the rebellious Southern states. Lincoln was reelected in 1864. In April 1865, five days after the Confederates surrendered, John Wilkes Booth shot him while he was at the theater. He died the next morning.

  He was the first president of the United States to be assassinated.

- **Questions answered and unanswered**: What is on the other side of the sky? Since the beginning of mankind, people have followed the solar system. In the 1900s, many questions were answered.

Milestones in the US Space Program

1958: The first US satellite (Explorer 1) was launched. 1961: Alan B. Shepard Jr. became first

American in space.

1962: John H. Glenn became the first American to orbit the earth.

1969: Neil A. Armstrong and Edwin E. Aldrin Jr. became the first people to land on the moon.

But man has never found the other side of the sky.

PART FIVE

CHAPTER

THIRTY-THREE

Return to Texas

There was only one reason War Eagle and Little Bear left their comfortable life in San Francisco. As War Eagle called into the wind, "Hold on, Sam Houston; your boys are coming home."

Traveling the same trail they had taken west, the pair rode south through the Joaquin Valley. Eleven years had passed since their journey took them north to the gold fields of California.

Since 1850, the pristine landscape nestled between the mountains had changed. It was no longer a lonely road.

Fleeing the perils of Civil War or searching for a pot of gold, pioneers fought dangers to reach the fertile farmland of this valley.

On many days, War Eagle and Little Bear said good-bye to pioneers going toward the setting sun. The two friends continued their ride into the rising light of day.

The more travelers they encountered, the worse the news of the Civil War became. There were all kinds of rumors about Texas and Sam Houston, and they were disturbing enough to make these two Indian sons push passed the pain of their aging bodies to cross the Great Plains as fast as possible.

Arriving in Texas was not the end of the road. Along the way, when they asked where they could find Sam Houston, they got different answers. Some people were hostile, accusing Houston of being against Texas because he did not support the Confederacy.

Others praised him for not wanting to send their men to war.

War Eagle and Little Bear were confused and eager to hear Father Sam's side of the story. Whatever it was, one thing was certain: these two Cherokee would never question or judge the wisdom of the man their people called the Raven.

Each day anxiety grew after the Houston household heard the news that War Eagle and little Bear were looking for them.

After riding through the hills in Huntsville, they reached their destination. Sam Houston, his wife, Margaret, and their eight children were living in a steamboat house at Cedar Point on Trinity Bay. The family's response to War Eagle and Little Bear's appearance was, "Welcome home."

The Houstons had often talked about the two and instilled in their children the knowledge of Houston's adopted Cherokee heritage.

After Houston scolded War Eagle and Little Bear for not being in touch with him for so many years, he recounted his story of those years. When he last saw War Eagle and Little Bear in 1840, he was the president of the Republic of Texas. After the annexation of Texas by the United States in 1845, Houston was elected to the US Senate. He served from February 21, 1846, until March 4, 1859.

During his term in the Senate, Houston spoke out against the growing sectionalism of the country. In a passionate speech, Houston said, "A nation divided against itself cannot stand." Eight years later, US President, Abraham Lincoln would express the same sentiment.

In 1859, Houston was elected governor of Texas. He opposed the secession of Texas from the Union. When an elected convention voted to secede from the United States on February 1, 1861, and Texas joined the Confederate States of America on March 2, 1861, Houston refused to recognize its legality. But the Texas legislature upheld the legitimacy of secession.

Sam Houston refused to take an oath of loyalty to the Confederacy, and he was evicted from office as governor of Texas on March 16, 1861. Houston chose not to resist, stating, "I love Texas too well to bring civil strife and bloodshed upon her. To avert this calamity, I shall make no endeavor to maintain my authority as chief executive of this state except by the peaceful exercise of my functions..."

After leaving the governor's mansion, Houston traveled to Galveston. Along the way, many people demanded an explanation for his refusal to support the Confederacy. On April 19, 1861, from a hotel window, he told a crowd:

Let me tell you what is coming. After the sacrifice of countless millions of treasure and hundreds of thousands of lives, you may win Southern independence if God be not against you, but I doubt it. I tell you that, while I, believe with you in the doctrine of states' rights, the North is determined to preserve this Union. They are not a fiery impulsive people as you are, for they live in colder climates. But when they begin to move in a given direction, they move with the steady momentum and perseverance of a mighty avalanche; and what I fear is they will overwhelm the South.

Seven days before Houston made this speech, the American Civil War between the North and South had begun.

***

CHAPTER

THIRTY-FOUR

War Marks Changes

Triggering the start of the American Civil War, Confederate troops fired on Fort Sumter, South Carolina.

"Children, listen to me," Sam Houston said to War Eagle, Little Bear, and the others. "This is not your war. I choose it not to be my war, but I am fearful it will reach our door."

Houston still controlled the room with his presence, and his authority demanded respect, but his delivery was less forceful and milder in tone. No longer was he the rough-and-ready warlord fighting for the rights of the Cherokee Nation and riding his horse for freedom in Texas.

His wisdom and reasoning prevailed; no one from the Houston household would go to fight in a war that was not of their making.

"War Eagle, you are too old to fight in any war," teased his friend, Little Bear.

"No, I am not," War Eagle insisted. "I am as strong as an ox." The war in the East seemed so very far away. How could War Eagle leave this man who had meant so much in his life? He would not.

Time in Texas had a way of standing still. Dignitaries from all around the country came to visit the elderly statesman. Margaret Houston was a gracious hostess, and it was easily recognized that she had tempering influence over her older husband.

Enjoying the time they spent with the new and improved Sam Houston, his two Cherokee children helped with family chores. Little Bear taught the Sequoyah Cherokee alphabet to the younger children, and War Eagle focused on their strength for fighting and good, strong character.

As the American Civil War raged on, normal life continued for the Houston family in Texas. But seasons have a way of changing everything.

In the summer of 1863, Sam Houston's health deteriorated due to a persistent cough. In mid-July, he developed pneumonia. This was one war that was his alone, and he would not win it. Sam Houston died on July 26, 1863.

All who knew him grieved over his death. Several years would pass before War Eagle and Little Bear felt as though they could leave the Houston family.

Margaret Houston never forgot the last words her husband said to her, "Texas, Texas, Margaret…" She wondered what words he had spoken to Little Bear. Had he told Little Bear about Polly? Sensing the restlessness of her two Cherokee children, Mrs. Houston approached Little Bear. "My intent is not to embarrass you," she began the conversation. "What I would like to know from you is, before my husband passed away did he…" She paused.

Little Bear did not wait for her to continue. "Yes, he told me about his meeting Polly in Alabama."

"Are you angry that we did not tell you before?" asked Margaret.

"No, I am not angry. I accept without question his judgment in not telling me where I could find Polly. He did say that it was not your decision not to tell me. I am comforted in knowing that Polly has such a good friend as you. To know she is cared for gives me peace of mind. At the same time, to know that I am not the one caring for her breaks my heart."

Reaching into his small leather pouch, Little Bear gently removed the red ribbon. As Margaret listened to Little Bear talk about Polly, the love of his life, she remembered the day when Polly invited her into her bedroom. There, she opened the little drawer of a bedside table and removed her Bible. From her Bible, she lifted the red ribbon.

Mrs. Houston had seen it in their eyes and heard it from their lips. Polly and Little Bear, whose love was everlasting, were forever connected by this red ribbon of time.

Because of her trusted friendship, Margaret Houston was the only person besides Little Bear and Polly to see the two separate pieces of the red ribbon.

Time has a way of changing everything. Whether measured by a ribbon, war, or life and death. In 1865, it was time for War Eagle and Little Bear to move on.

CHAPTER

THIRTY-FIVE

Back to Tahlequah

"If you leave, who will teach us how to make the Cherokee letters? And who will teach us how to shoot a bow and arrow and how to be strong and brave like Uncle War Eagle?" The children of Margaret and Sam Houston called the two Cherokee men "uncle" because they were well aware that the men were too old to be their true brothers.

The children's questions would not go unanswered. War Eagle explained, "You must go to school to learn to be smart in Cherokee ways and white man's ways. You must listen to you mother. She will teach you how to be strong and brave like your father."

Visiting the Houston household in Texas, several Union officers offered their respect in appreciation of Sam Houston's support of the Union.

The officers were pleased to convey that the Confederacy had surrendered to the Union. The American Civil War was over.

Noticing the two Cherokee among the Houston household, the Union soldiers were puzzled.

"These gentlemen are my husband's children," Margaret Houston proudly proclaimed. She had a keen eye for such things.

Margaret did have a question for the Union officers, however. "What brings you to Texas?"

"We are leading our regiment to Fort Gibson, near a place called Tahlequah, Indian Territory."

Looking at War Eagle and Little Bear, the officer asked, "Do you know of such a place?"

"Tahlequah," said War Eagle. "Yes, it is the place where we once lived. Perhaps it is time for us to go home."

One of the Union officers questioned this decision. "I am not sure you want to go there. The place is a mess."

"We helped build it once before. We can do it again," replied Little Bear.

Looking the fifty-three-year-old Cherokee up and down, the officer smiled. "If you say so. You are welcome to go with my regiment as far as Fort Gibson. You can ride in one of our covered wagons or get yourself a horse."

Remembering the long ride on horseback from California to Texas, Little Bear did not hesitate in taking the offer to ride in a wagon.

On the morning of departure, tearful good-byes were made with the Houston family. Then, the regiment moved out in perfect formation, headed for the Red River. War Eagle rode tall in the saddle of a black stallion.

Reaching Fort Gibson, War Eagle and Little Bear purchased a wagon, horses, and supplies to continue their trip to Tahlequah. Mrs. Houston had been very generous in giving them the means for living until they were settled.

It wasn't until the two friends left Fort Gibson that they confronted their memories of Tahlequah.

Seeking freedom from a past of heartaches, they'd hoped that by running away, they could lose their pain of their wives' deaths. Seventeen years had passed. What had happened to the place they left all those years ago?

Since the final removal of the Indians to land west of the Mississippi River, things had gone well for the Cherokee Nation settlers in Tahlequah, Oklahoma. In 1861, the Cherokee way of life was interrupted by the growing tensions between the Northern and Southern states. Then the American Civil War began. Surely, the Cherokee Nation need not take part in this Civil War between the Northern and Southern states.

John Ross, the chief of the Cherokee, spoke to the Cherokee Nation on the importance of remaining neutral in this battle.

Another Cherokee, Stand Waite, put together a regiment authorized by the Southern states known as the Confederacy.

Chief John Ross feared that the Cherokee Nation would become divided with Cherokee fighting Cherokee, just as American Southerners were fighting American Northerners.

John Ross asked for and got Union troops sent to the Indian Territory, but the area around Tahlequah remained in the hands of Confederates under the leadership of Stand Waite.

In the winter of 1862–1863, Union victories ran Stand Waite out of the Tahlequah area. When it looked like all was lost for the Confederacy, Stand Waite led vengeance raids into Tahlequah, burning the Cherokee capital and the home of Chief John Ross.

On April 9, 1865, Confederate General Robert E. Lee surrendered to Union General Ulysses S. Grant at Appomattox, Virginia. The war was over—sort of. Stand Waite did not surrender until June 23, 1865.

The city of Tahlequah was left in ruins.

CHAPTER

THIRTY-SIX

Rebuilding Tahlequah

Returning home was like a dream, only this was a nightmare.

The sounds of war were gone; the scene of war was not. Left on this battlefield were many widowed women, and the number of orphaned children was staggering.

Burned-out homes, slaughtered stock, fields over grown with weeds and bramble...The Cherokee of Tahlequah, Oklahoma, found themselves destitute. It did not matter which side of American Civil War they had been on. Refuges or not, they all had to start over.

War Eagle and Little Bear allowed themselves only a moment of despair; there was no time for self-pity or thoughts of yesteryear.

War Eagle proclaimed, "We can fix this." Little Bear responded, "We must fix this."

The Cherokee people had survived being moved from their homeland by the white man of the eastern United States. They would not be destroyed by a war of southern white man vs. northern white man, a civil war not of the Cherokee.

Once again, the Cherokee people would work side by side with strength and resilience to rebuild their homes and their shattered lives.

With the help of War Eagle and Little Bear, the unit of the Cherokee Nation would be whole again. All talked of memories and names. They did not share emotions; only dedication in rebuilding Tahlequah.

By 1867, the Cherokee Nation had thirty-two public schools back in operation. The public library was restored and a series of schoolbooks in the Cherokee language and alphabet were being produced.

Defining the times, the publication of the Cherokee Advocate Newspaper was resumed. Progress in the Tahlequah area was fast. The life-giving cycles of the Cherokee Nation were not over.

On opening day of the new, two-story, brick capital building, War Eagle sat with Little Bear on the porch of the new house they had built.

Wondering aloud, War Eagle said, "They say everything will be all right in the end. Is this the end?"

From inside the house, a voice answered, "It is not the end until I say so."

It was Old Man Charlie.

Historical Facts

- **Texas**: Six flags have flown over Texas since Spanish explorers arrived in 1519. These were the flags of Spain, France, Mexico, the Republic of Texas, the United States, and the Confederacy. American colonists won independence from Mexico in 1836 and created a republic before joining the United States on December 29, 1845.

- **Sam Houston**: A timeline of his life:

  1832–1836: Houston lived in Nacogdoches, Texas, and worked as a lawyer.

  1835: In November 1835, he was commissioned a major general in the Texas army.

  1836: On March 2, he signed the Texas Declaration of Independence.

1836: On April 21, he defeated Mexico President Antonio Lopez de Santa Anna at the Battle of San Jacinto.

1836: On September 5, he was elected president of Republic of Texas, an office he held twice, serving from October 22, 1836 to December 10, 1838, and again from December 12, 1841, to December 9, 1844.

1840: On May 9, Houston, age forty-seven, married for the third time. The bride was twenty- one-year-old Margaret Moffette Lea of Marion, Alabama. The marriage lasted longer than his two previous unions had and produced eight children born between Houston's fiftieth and sixty-seventh years.

1846: From February 21, 1846, until March 4, 1859, Houston served as United States senator from Texas.

1859: He was elected governor of Texas.

He was the only person in US history to serve as governor of two states. Early in his career, he served as governor of Tennessee.

1861: On March 16, he was evicted from office for refusing to take an oath of loyalty to the Confederacy.

1862: Houston rented a steamboat house in Huntsville, Texas. The hills in Huntsville reminded him of his home in Tennessee.

1863: His health deteriorated and he developed pneumonia. He died on July 26, 1863. Many monuments, museums, statues, and streets in the United States are named after Sam Houston.

The grave of Sam Houston is in Huntsville, Texas.

- **Sam Houston's children**:

Sam Houston Jr., 1843–1894

Nancy Elizabeth Houston, 1846–1920 (named after her grandmother)

Margaret Lea Houston, 1848–1906

Mary William Houston, 1850–1931

Antoinette Power Houston, 1851–1932 (named after Margaret's sister)

Andrew Jackson Houston, 1854–1941 (became a US senator from Texas)

William Rogers Houston, 1858–1891

Temple Lea Houston, 1860–1905 (named after Margaret's father; served as a senator in the Texas legislature 1885–1888)

- **The American Civil War**: (1861–1865) Fought between the states of the Confederacy and the northern states of the Union. The Confederacy believed that states had the right to make their own laws without interference from the federal government. The Union wanted total control, especially over abolishing slavery. On April 12, 1861, the war began. After four years, the war ended with over 600,000 Americans dead. The Union was preserved after the Confederacy surrendered in 1865.

- **John Ross**: b. 10/3/1790, d. 8/1/1866. He was principal chief of the Cherokee Native American Nation from 1828 to 1866. He led the Cherokee through tumultuous years of development, relocation to Oklahoma, and the American Civil War. He is buried in Park Hill, Oklahoma, where his gravestone inscription reads. "John Ross served the Cherokee people as Principal Chief for 38 years. From 1828- 1866, he led us through times of Great Achievement and Great Sorrow."

- **Stand Waite**: A Cherokee Indian who signed the Treaty of New Echota in 1835. He became a general in the Confederate Army during the Civil War. He was the last Confederate general to surrender to the Union. He claimed to be the principal chief of the Confederate Cherokee Nation. The population of the Cherokee Nation before the Civil War was estimated at 18,000. At the end of the war, it was 13,500.

United States Presidents from 1865–1877

- **Andrew Johnson**: b. 12/29/1808 in Raleigh, North Carolina; d. 7/ 31/1875 at Carter Station, Tennessee; term of office: 1865–1869. Jackson was Abraham Lincoln's vice-president, and became the seventeenth president of the United States when Lincoln was assassinated in 1865. Jackson stuck rigidly to his policies during the Reconstruction period that followed the Civil War. He was the only president never to have gone to school. He was a self-taught scholar, a member of the US House of Representatives, the governor of Tennessee, and a US senator.

- **Ulysses S. Grant**: b. 4/22/1822, d. 7/23/1885; term of office: 1869–1877. Grant was the eighteenth United States president. As a Union general, he led his troops to victory in crucial battles in the Civil War. His success as a Union commander made him popular, which probably helped him to win the presidency.

CHAPTER

THIRTY-SEVEN

Old Man Charlie

Resting in the shade of an old oak tree, he sat not on the ground but on a large rock. The long, gray hair about his shoulders and the lines in his face revealed his long life. His body was worn from hard work, heartache, and trying times—all reasons to be bitter.

Fears were hidden inside this old Cherokee Indian as he greeted strangers with a spontaneous show of warmth and grace.

As soon as War Eagle and Little Bear dismounted their horses, he rose to meet them. "Hello, strangers. They call me Old Man Charlie. Haven't seen you fellows in Tahlequah before."

"Years ago I lived in the house that stood behind the old oak tree," said War Eagle. "Today, I see only ashes there."

Old Man Charlie walked close to look upon War Eagle's face. "You must be the one Billy called War Eagle. He said you would return one day."

"Yes, today is that day. I am War Eagle, and this man here with me is Little Bear. Little Bear is my wife's brother, and Billy was the brother of Little Bear's wife."

Old Man Charlie held his hands up. "Whoa, I don't reason all that, just that Billy said the house he lived in belonged to War Eagle."

Could it be that Billy died in the fire that burned his house down? War Eagle asked, "Did Billy, I mean, how did—"

"No, no," Old Man Charlie quickly responded. "Billy rode off to fight in the big war in the East. Soon after, the white men— rebels, they called them— burned the house down. Billy was not here for the house burning, but I hear he died fighting in the war."

It took a few minutes for War Eagle to regain his composure. He tried not to remember all the times he; his wife, Tamara; Billy; Little Bear; and his wife, Window Bird had sat around the old oak tree talking, laughing, and teasing Billy because he was a lawyer. Billy, the Cherokee lawyer, was going to right all the wrongs.

"I'm very sorry for your loss," said Old Man Charlie. "If you and your friend need a place to say, you are welcome in my home. Just me, no Mrs., no dogs, no cats. Good clean bed, and I'll even cook you supper."

War Eagle didn't have to answer. "We'll take it!" shouted Little Bear. The three Cherokee laughed.

They spent many hours talking. War Eagle told Old Man Charlie his life's story, and Little Bear was eager to tell all about his life. Missing was Old Man Charlie's story. The two Cherokee friends would never know where he came from, what his real name was, or how old he was. When they asked him these questions, his reply was, "I am a good cook."

"Yes, you are a great cook," they answered without hesitation. "Then that is all you need to know," Old Man Charlie said, and he always had the final word.

War Eagle, the strong, brave Cherokee; and Little Bear, a Cherokee teacher; followed Old Man Charlie, warrior of wisdom, down the road to his home.

End of day or end of a journey. Their first road taken led War Eagle and Little Bear out of Texas to Tahlequah; then to Missouri, to California, back to Texas, and finally to Tahlequah again.

All that happened along that road was the life of War Eagle. He carried the dream of his father, Sky Walker, always searching for the other side of the sky.

Now, his journey had brought him to the doorstep of Old Man Charlie. Time would now be spent helping others rebuild their Cherokee Nation in Tahlequah. In turn, many had roles to play in building a new house for War Eagle.

As evening shadows crossed the porch, the whippoorwill called from a nearby thicket; the cool breeze tossed a lonely leaf across the yard.

Gazing at the stars, War Eagle embraced his memories, often humming a familiar tune of the Red River Valley.

He was War Eagle, Texas Cherokee.

CHAPTER

THIRTY-EIGHT

A Visitor

The sun rose, giving light to a new day. Old Man Charlie made a fire in the kitchen stove, readied the coffee, and put the bacon in the frying pan. All these actions were routine for Old Man Charlie since he came to live with War Eagle and Little Bear in their new house.

Routine was about to change. On this day, nothing was going to be routine,

"Stranger coming, stranger coming," Old Man Charlie muttered to himself.

Resonating throughout the house, the stranger's voice shouted from the yard, "Hello inside the house. I saw your smoke coming out of the chimney and smelled your bacon from a mile away. I hope I have come to the right place."

"What place would that be," Old Man Charlie asked when he opened the front door.

Coming closer to the porch, the stranger replied, "Home of my brothers, War Eagle and Little Bear."

Dismounting his horse, tying the reins to a hitching post, stepping upon the porch, the stranger waited for an answer.

What he got was the slamming shut of the front door.

Taking a close look at the stranger, Old Man Charlie was quick to decide that this man standing on the porch was no brother to the two Cherokee that lived in this house. His face, stature, and dress revealed that he was a white man.

Pouring himself a cup of coffee, War Eagle called from the kitchen, "What is all that racket out there, Charlie?"

"Some white man saying he is your brother." Old Man Charlie just barely got the words out of his mouth when Little Bear burst by him to open the front door.

"Sam Houston Jr., what are you doing on my front porch?" Spilling his coffee as the cup crashed on the floor, War Eagle raced through the doorway, and grabbed Sam Houston Jr., lifting him into the air.

Puzzled, Old Man Charlie watched the greeting; the laughter and backslapping continued from some time. Running out of patience for an explanation, he said loudly, "What do you mean, Sam Houston? This man is not old enough to be Sam Houston."

"No," said War Eagle. "This brother is the son of the great Sam Houston. You can call him Junior."

Turning to Sam Houston Jr., War Eagle introduced Old Man Charlie.

"OK, I know his name. I do not know why you call him brother. I am not so old as to fail to recognize that a white man is not a Cherokee brother." Old Man Charlie was curious.

"Poor Charlie," said Little Bear. "Let's eat breakfast while we tell him the story of three Houston brothers."

After listening to all the talking and laughter at breakfast, Old Man Charlie concluded that the three were brothers—a little crazy, but brothers by choice.

War Eagle and Little Bear had plenty of questions for Sam Jr. How was Mrs. Houston doing and what about each of the children? Most of the day went by before they finally got around to asking the real reason that Sam Jr. had sought out his brothers.

"I know it was a surprise, my showing up in your front yard the way I did," Sam Jr. began to explain. "Mother sent me to ask Little Bear to go on a trip with me. She thinks it is time for Little Bear to go to Alabama to be with Polly and to unite the red ribbon."

War Eagle looked surprised. "The red ribbon? How do you know about the red ribbon?"

"Are you kidding?" Sam smiled. "Once Mother told our sisters, the story was out, and you can believe all of Texas knows by now."

Without saying a word, Little Bear walked across the yard into a nearby thicket of trees.

"Should we follow him?" asked Sam.

"No, we do not." Old Man Charlie was adamant.

"Well, how long will he be in the thicket? I

need to know if he is going to Alabama with me." Sam was anxious.

"Relax," War Eagle told him. "Little Bear will return after the fish are caught, cleaned, and Old Man Charlie has supper on the table. No matter what, Little Bear never misses a meal."

More stories were told; the fish platter was emptied; the end of the day found them all resting on the front porch.

The quiet of the night settled in. Only an owl broke the silence now and again.

There had been no talk of a trip to Alabama.

CHAPTER

THIRTY-NINE

Standing on the Riverbank

At the break of dawn, it was Old Man Charlie in the barn preparing the horses and wagon; it was Old Man Charlie not joining the others for breakfast; it was Old Man Charlie packing the wagon; it was Old Man Charlie who answered Sam Houston Jr.'s question, "Is Little Bear going to Alabama?"

Body bending from the winds of time, Old Man Charlie reached for Little Bear's hand. "The spirit goes with you; walk your journey to the end—a place where time that existed shall meet."

"Thank you, Charlie." Little Bear embraced his dear friend. "You take care of yourself and take care of War Eagle. Don't let him get into trouble."

"Myself will be just fine," said Old Man Charlie. "War Eagle has to learn to take care of himself."

Saying their farewells, Little Bear and Sam Houston Jr. settled themselves in the wagon in which War Eagle would take them to the steamboat on the Arkansas River. Sam left his horse with Old Man Charlie, telling him to keep it because one never knew when someone would need a good horse.

Old Man Charlie stood in the yard watching the wagon until it was out of sight.

***

A full day of conversation began with Little Bear saying to War Eagle, "You do know you will need to stay out of trouble."

From then on, the conversation was one-sided as War Eagle reminded Little Bear how, time and time again, it was War Eagle doing the saving when his friend was in trouble.

"If I remember correctly, it was me who saved your scalp when we made that Mexican, Santa Anna, surrender to our father, Sam Houston.

"Remember those days down in Texas? We were young and brave; even tried to swim across the Red River."

"No," said Little Bear, "you tried to swim. I stayed on my horse."

War Eagle talked about all the years and all the times except when he was married to Tamara, Little Bear's sister, and when Little Bear was married to Window Bird. These memories were still too painful.

Listening to War Eagle, Sam Houston Jr. had few words to say. His mind was on the long trip ahead. The road to the boat ramp on the Arkansas River was a good day's ride away. They would be into the night before the wagon came to a stop within walking distance of the steamboat.

Sitting by the campfire, Sam Jr. told stories of trips to Alabama he had taken with his father and mother. Those were happy times, but the Civil War had changed all that. The death of his father left Sam Jr. with no choice but to go to Alabama and bring the family that had survived the war to Texas.

The wisdom of Sam Jr.'s mother was to unite enduring love.

He was to take Little Bear to Polly in Alabama.

Past midnight, under the stars, Sam Houston Jr. had plans for a long journey. Little Bear was comforted in knowing that he was following his heart. The darkness brought no rest for War Eagle.

He could not see his future. As dawn broke, a morning mist hung over the river, shrouding the riverboat landing. Sam Jr. boarded the boat.

A moment in time found two Cherokee friends having to face a farewell.

Little Bear, a Cherokee from the eastern lands, had crossed the Mississippi River to meet War Eagle, Cherokee of the west.

On this day neither had the courage to say good-bye.

As the steamboat pulled away from the dock and slowly faded from view, War Eagle was left standing on the riverbank.

CHAPTER FORTY

Where to from Here?

Sitting on the wagon seat, guiding the horses, War Eagle talked only to the wind.

"Carry me where I need to be and show me what my future holds. For now, I travel a lonely road, and my heart does not understand."

War Eagle had always been symbolic of what it meant to be Cherokee. He'd had special gifts from the time that he was very young, but he had to learn what the gifts were and what to do with them.

He would now have to use his living and learning experiences. In his life, he had crossed many bridges. On this day, it was time to listen intently for the sound of spirits and seek a vision of direction.

As day became night, the road ended where it

began. Old Man Charlie was asleep when War Eagle entered the house.

When night became day, Old Man Charlie made fire in the stove, prepared the coffee, and cooked bacon for two people.

Nothing was asked, and nothing was answered. It was easy to see that both War Eagle and Old Man Charlie were having a hard time with the departure of Little Bear.

Understanding the reason for Little Bear's journey to Alabama did not make them miss him any less.

As the sun set in the west and dusk turned to night, the owl called from the thicket nearby, the wolf howled from far away, and fireflies flashed in the mist hanging over the yard; the chair on the porch was empty.

There was no chatter of friends telling stories and no laughter. Few words were spoken between War Eagle and Old Man Charlie. Old Man Charlie left the porch early in the night; War Eagle was left all alone.

The chores were not neglected. War Eagle was diligent in his work and always too tired to be social with friends.

"Are your lips broken?" asked Old Man Charlie.

"No," replied War Eagle. "Why do you ask a thing like that?"

"Just wondering," Old Man Charlie explained. "I don't hear you whistling anymore. Used to you whistled when you did anything and even when you were doing nothing."

"I guess I have lost my whistler," said War Eagle. "I don't seem to be able to find anything anymore."

"Perhaps it is time for you to find yourself," advised Old Man Charlie.

Possessing the spirit of the Cherokee, Old Man Charlie had lived many years following the teachings of his ancestors.

With the sound of raindrops softly pattering on leaves on a cool rainy night, sitting in his rocker on the porch, across from War Eagle, it was time for Old Man Charlie to give his wisdom to someone in need.

He began,

"Our lives have four directions: east, south,

north, and west. The sun rises each day in the east, bathing our world and all living things in warmth and light.

"From the east the sun brings a new day. Flowers bend toward the sun's light as plants and animals embrace each new beginning. We all grow strong and flourish under the sun's umbrella.

"In the south, we look for our survival. The earth of the south gives us plants, trees, and greenery, providing food to eat, shelter to protect us, and tools for our use. As the southlands give us all things, we need to live and grow, we must nurture and care for our earth.

"To the west we see the setting sun, the end of another day. The western horizon is a peaceful place, a still surface of wondrous beauty. Our minds are at rest, feeling purification and healing in the gentleness and infinite strength of the west.

"Winds of the north carry our thoughts forward. It is the wind that takes away uncertainty and fear, bringing us solitude and strength. The destructive energy of the wind is always replaced by the wind's spirit of quiet wisdom.

"Your pathway for seeking these directions of the east, south, north, and west can be found in the footsteps of your ancestors."

From his beginning, War Eagle had learned from his grandmother and then from his Uncle Bowles. Now he listened to another sacred spirit.

Rain was now falling steadily; the hour was late in the night.

Old Man Charlie sat in his rocking chair, all alone.

The early morning mist on his face, a lone rider guided his horse down the road: War Eagle in search of his soul.

CHAPTER

FORTY-ONE

Finding Home Again

At the crossroads where the four directions meet, War Eagle traveled in search of the place where he belonged.

Days turned to weeks. At age fifty-seven, his journey wearying, the trail he followed led him home.

Home is where the story begins, but not always where it ends.

For War Eagle, home had not been a place but a feeling. From Texas to Oklahoma to California and back, home was the ground upon which he walked.

Every mile traveled, his ancestors walked with him. His past was always in his heart. At trail's end, he found home.

Crossing the Red River, he beheld the Red River Valley.

His tears flowed freely as though cleansing his soul. Riding into the valley, War Eagle sensed that he had come out of the shade into the sun again.

The Red River Valley of Texas was the place where the Texas Cherokee had made their home for many years. On this day, War Eagle, Texas Cherokee, returned to his birthplace.

On this day, he found peace, a sense of joy, and a power within from his ancestors, eternally in his heart.

Every Texas Cherokee carried the spirit of the Red River Valley with him. In finding home, War Eagle came to know and to understand that the spirits of his ancestors would never leave him.

Each day that he was blessed with the sights and experiences of another day, he was not alone.

Exploring the land of his childhood, War Eagle spent most of his time along the river. He fished the waters and listened for the scream of the eagle. On many days, the eagle soared so close to War Eagle that each could look into the other's eyes. He felt a lasting kinship, just as he did with the land, lasting forever.

Gleaming in the morning sun, a heavy mist hung over the valley. War Eagle sat on the bank of the Red River.

Casually, Little Bear walked up behind him.

"What took you so long?" War Eagle asked without turning around.

"How did you know it was me?" asked Little Bear.

"Does one not know the footsteps of an old friend?" replied War Eagle.

After several hours of each explaining the hows and whys of being there in the Red River Valley, War Eagle asked the big question.

"Tell me, Little Bear, did you find what you were looking for in Alabama?"

Facing away from this friend, Little Bear replied, "My time has not ended, but the journey of the red ribbon is over."

As the sun sat on the western horizon, the two Cherokee who became brothers when Sam Houston called them his sons, talked until the coals in the campfire turned cold. They spoke of good times, bad times, laughed, cried, and agreed that what they both needed most at that time was Old Man Charlie's cooking. For them, Old Man Charlie was home.

War Eagle pledged that his soul forever would be a part of the Red River Valley. Just as the river flows through this Texas valley, the lives of these two Cherokee would continue until it was time for them to join their ancestors on the other side of the sky.

Interesting Facts

- **Red River Valley**: The verdant Red River Valley of Texas is the location where many Cherokee Indians settled after being forced from their traditional homes and lands in Georgia, Tennessee, and the Carolinas by the United States government. For nearly one hundred years, the Red River Cherokee fought for recognition by the United States government, but they were continually rebuked due to the tribe's refusal to be incorporated into the larger Cherokee Nation, based in Oklahoma.

- **Tribal members organized the United Red River Band (URRB)** and it became the largest Native American organization in northeast Texas. Fiercely independent, the Red River Cherokee people consider themselves to be autonomous, self-governing, and sovereign. The URRB will not permit gambling of any kind on tribal land. It will not resort to that means for financial benefit.

  The URRB has more than 1,500 recognized tribal members. It is estimated that as many as 40,000 certifiable descendants of Red River Cherokee are scattered throughout the United States, Mexico, and Canada.

- **Lawsuits over land**: From the 1840s until the 1960s, the Cherokee sought compensation from Texas for the lands they lost in 1839. All claims were unsuccessful. In 1963, the Cherokee petitioned the state of Texas for redress of the 1839 grievances, asking for compensation in the form of free education for a thousand Cherokee in state-supported Texas universities. But Texas Attorney General Waggoner Carr denied the validity of Cherokee claim on the grounds that the state of Texas was not liable for claims against the Republic of Texas.

- **Land ownership** was the most basic need of the Anglo- Americans. Seven times as many people live in New York City today as occupied all of North America north of Mexico when Columbus arrived in 1492.

Author's Note

The spirit of the Cherokee is found in the enduring love and friendship of the characters in my books.

For the life story of Little Bear read, *Ribbon of Time* by Martha Lou Perritti.

For the life story of Polly, read *Standing Against the Wind* by Martha Lou Perritti.

I remember the first time I went to Oklahoma. Walking out of the airport in Oklahoma City, I marveled, "Look at the sky, it is sooo big!"

I wonder what is on the other side of the sky.

References

Conley, Robert J., *The Cherokee Nation: A History*, (Albuquerque, New Mexico: University of New Mexico Press, 2005).

Eastman, Charles Ohiyesa, *Living in Two Worlds: The American Indian Experience,* (Bloomington, Indiana: World Wisdom Inc., 2010).

Garrett, Michael, *Walking on the Wind: Cherokee Teachings for Harmony and Balance,* (Rochester, Vermont: Bear & Company Publishing, 1998).

Perritti, Martha Lou, *Ribbon of Time: Little Bear's Journey*, (West Suffield, Connecticut: Lifestyles Press, 2012).

Shapiro, William E., editor, *The Young Peoples Encyclopedia of the United States,* (Brookfield, Connecticut: Millbrook Press, 1992).